COVENTRY VOICES

COVENTRY VOICES

Tim Lewis

The results of a project over several months in 1987, in
Coventry, sponsored by West Midlands Arts and the
Coventry City Council.

Published by Red Horse Publications in association with the Self
Publishing Association Limited

ISBN 1 85421 001 2

The publisher acknowledges financial assistance from West
Midlands Arts and the Coventry City Council towards both the
project and the publication of this book.

"Wood End – The Positive Things" and the photograph on page 104
first appeared in "People to People".

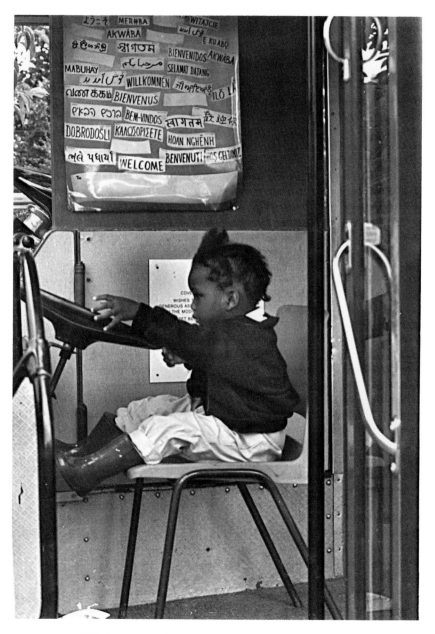

'Welcome to the Buzz – Coventry's mobile
nursery.'

For
Tom Mann

INTRODUCTION

Coventry, like most British cities, has been hit badly by the recession of the last ten years. More than most, it has suffered from unemployment and cuts in social provision, which have put the social fabric of the city under great strain.

In response, the people of Coventry have retained their humour and resilience. Many people in the city have begun to come together as government provision for care has been cut, into tenants' associations, self-help organisations, charities and schemes such as the elderly watch in Stoke Aldermoor. This book deals with the social impact on city life of the last few years and how people are adapting to those changes, how they see the city and how they have come to terms with the way it has changed. Coventry is now, in many industries, a low wage city, when once it led the country. Much of it is still prosperous. Areas, especially in the south and parts of the north-west, have seen a rise in living standards, but there are growing pockets of deprivation, mainly in the north and east. Coventry is, above all, now a city of contrasts.

"Coventry Voices" is for the people of Coventry, a unique record of their lives and views. Many of the names have been changed, but all the stories are based on actual statements made to me. Needless to say, I do not agree personally with everything said.

The book is the result of a project carried out during the summer of 1987 and was funded by West Midlands Arts and the Coventry City Council. I am extremely grateful to them for their support. I should like to thank Arthur Waugh (Senior), Dave Edwards, George Lindfield and Catherine Davies for their advice. But above all, I offer my warmest thanks to the many hundreds of Coventry people whom I interviewed and who helped me achieve this book.

CONTENTS

	Page No
The Old Cathedral	11
The Canal Basin	13
Paradise Amusements	14
The Punk	14
The Post Office Queue	15
Working the Pictures	19
Pool Meadow	24
Councillor Arthur Waugh, Senior	25
In This City	29
On an Island	30
From Pillar to Post	34
Kay	40
Glue Sniffing	45
Playing Table Tennis	49
A Teenager's Reply	55
Saturday Night Fever	58
Pigeon Parade	61
Mummy, I Want a Wee Wee . . .	63
The Incontinent Laundry Service	65
Nursery Nurse	72
The Women's Shelter	75
The Bingo Player	81
Mr Big	86
Hawking	86
Hand-out	87
Sainsbury's	87
The Forgotten Ones	88
Jacko	89
One Man – Nine Lives	91
The Old Man	99
Signing On	105
The Notice Board	111
The End of the World Will Be On Friday	114

The West Indian Luncheon Club 121
The St Barnabas Centre 123
The Interview 127
Of Hammers and Shovels 133
Mr Singh, Mr Singh and Mr Singh 136
Maqsood 143
Mr Kartar Singh and Mrs Pritam Kaur 151
Mrs Banti Kaur 152
Toni, Harjinder and Shamshad 156
Lady Herbert's Garden 164
The Auction Room 166
The S.A.S. Postman 170
The Buzz 176
The Wholefood Stall 177
The Amalgamated Engineering Union 180
Tower blocks and concrete . . . 182
Four snippets 183
Jim and the Telephone Box 184
Eddie and the Hillfields Tower Block Campaign 186
Woodend – Plans for a Pool Hall 190
Woodend – The Positive Things 194
Ball Hill and Styvechale 198
Stoke Aldermoor – Brendan 202
'What Ya Gonna Do About It?' 206
On the Bins 214
Tarquin Close né Ivy Walk 221
Three Scenes 222
It's a Dog's Life 224
The Buck Stops Here 226
The Old-Time Dance Hall 231
In the Co-op 233
The Age Concern Workshop 235
The Home Help 238
Go For It, City! 245

Map of Coventry

THE OLD CATHEDRAL

I am searching for you, Coventry,
Searching for your heart, your soul.
Where has it gone, city,
Where has it gone?

Is it here, Coventry?
In the ruins of the old cathedral,
To which I always turn
In my hours of self-doubt?

The modern, the prestigious, the sleek,
Overbears nearby,
But it lacks the soul, the meaning
Of the old.
It has style, it has art,
But it has no simple heart
In which I, in my simple need,
Can confide.

The new bells start their welcome,
Clamouring hope and aspiration,
Dulling my thoughts for a while.

I hear voices, whispering in the peals,
I see faces, lonely faces,
Staring down from empty tracery,
I see souls, questioning souls,
Wishing they had hands to guide my pen,
I see hearts, lost hearts,
Reaching from their burial to touch me.

I hear voices, crying to me,
Crying to be heard,
Crying of their hopes and pain.
I hear voices, voices, whispering, whispering.

11

I think that is you, Coventry,
The modern, the prestigious, the sleek,
Having turned your back on the old,
On your heart, your soul and your voice,
And I think, listening to your bells,
You now realise your mistake.

Frink sculpture in the Old Cathedral

THE CANAL BASIN

It's dawn by the canal basin, a party of school kids pile out of a minibus on the embankment by the sleek canal boat. The masters organise the unloading of sleeping bags and supplies for the week's trip and the excited children mill around, or delicately board the narrowboat to take a look inside its confined, dark and exciting interior.

The slim bunks amaze them, the galley, the toilet tucked away, the cupboards using every inch of crowded space, the duckboards along the sides, the painted rudder in red, the bow in white and black, the sleek body in sparkling green, the gaffs and ropes, the thought of sleeping on board, all enthrall, spell-bind and slightly frighten them.

They slowly load up and climb aboard, sorting out where to sleep and eat. The helmsman orders two to cast off, the engine chuggs into life and slowly the boat moves away from the newly-restored embankment walls, past the towering image of the large, renovated, wooden warehouse, with its rope pulleys and cranes, its store rooms and grain chutes, its pigeons nesting and painters still finishing the restoration work, under the first of many bridges. It passes a couple of kayaks messing around by the Outward Bound Centre, and heads for the main Grand Union.

PARADISE AMUSEMENTS

Entering Paradise Amusements, I see about ten teenage youths hanging around inside. Only three are actually playing the space invader machines. The others are leaning on the machines and watching, or sitting in a group, talking. They are suspicious of me as I walk into their territory and I feel their eyes and the stab of their belligerence in my back.

In the far corner is a snack bar, serving teas to another group of youths. It is Thursday afternoon. Not only do they all look as though they have been there all day, they look as though they'd been there all week. One lad, obviously just having cashed his giro, is shoving fifty pees into a fruit machine at an alarming rate.

I walk around the machines, all flashing their electronic messages and instructions, giving short sequences of the zapping pleasures to be had and showing impressive lists of the top six scorers. Even the fruit machines have gone electronic, with little green screens flashing up catchy phrases, enticing the punters to partake.

The electronic screams, zooms and explosions fill the air of the dark room. Up some infirm stairs, I can hear some people shooting pool. Noise. Lights. Excitement.

THE PUNK

A young gothic punk, with dyed white hair, old black jeans, plimsoles and a black leather jacket covered with studs, boards a bus for Cheylsemore. On the back of his jacket is a painting of a skull, in a sickly yellow-green, with sharpened teeth, blood dripping from it and two bulging, bloodshot eyes staring out. Around it is woven a green ribbon with the motto: "VOICE OF A GENERATION".

THE POST OFFICE QUEUE

It was little Tommy who started it. Totally by accident, you might say. He was only nine, but had learnt to draw by picking up a bit here and a bit there. He'd always liked doodling his scratchings on any odd piece of wallpaper or tablecloth that came his way. Felt tips mostly. Completely indelible felt tips that drove his mother up the wall. That, after all, was half the fun.

But felt tips were useless on brick walls. And magic markers soon dried out, even on concrete. Now billboards, yes. A magic marker was just perfect for them, but there weren't many between home and school. That was when he discovered chalks.

Blue, pink, green, yellow, brown, white, you name it. They came up really pretty and he could scrawl his space invaders and bombers and He Men on pavement and telephone box and shop doorway.

There was one particularly tempting space, large, clean, flat and readily reachable, a few shops down from the post office. It was a large board covering the window of an empty clothes' shop. It was so good he made the extra effort to rise earlier for school and get off before his three brothers and two sisters. They never had breakfast anyway and he slept on the outside of the bed, so they didn't care.

Those few minutes dawdling to school every morning had always made his day. But he had special plans for this new board. It was going to be his masterpiece. A grand fresco, properly planned and laid out. It was going to be the planet of Og. A huge volcano would rise up in the middle, spraying lava and smoke high into the air. There was going to be a terrible forest on one side and a deadly swamp on the other, crawling with crocodiles. And all about – the grand design – a battle between the Go-bots and the dinosaurs of Og!

As he chalked the volcano in browns, with streaks and swirls and plumes of red, he was oblivious to the growing queue outside the post office. The fact that it was Monday morning meant little to him, except the dazed end-of-weekend feel and a subconscious drive that somehow walked him to school. But to many people in Hillfields it meant child benefit day, giro cashing, or drawing on savings, often after a desperate Sunday with, not a sumptious dinner, but hardly a can of beans between five. And, worse for some, no money for fags! Such deprivation explained the demented, ravenous eyes and fidgeting frames of the lengthening queue.

At first, Tommy was a nuisance. A snotty, not particularly neat or clean boy, graffitiing the local area. But as the picture started to take shape, and the queue and its boredom grew, he became the unwitting centre of attraction.

'Hey, nipper, you could make a living at that,' said one. 'You should do it down the precinct. Get a tin or something, for the money.'

'He can't be more'n eight or nine. It ain't right. Ain't you got no school to go to?' asked another.

'Ow, shut it. Give the lad a coin. Go on.'

'I ain't got nothing. And if I had, I wouldn't waste it on him.'

'I've got ten pence. Here lad. What's your name then?'

'Tommy.' He was stunned by the money thrust into his hand.

'What is it?'

'Can't you see it's a volcano? Give the lad a chance.'

'Here. Here's twenty. Get yourself some sweets.'

'Ain't you got no school to go to?'

'Yea.'

'Well, you're late. Get off with you.'

Tommy stuffed his chalks into his pockets and hurried off. The money had a similar effect on him as the angel had on Saul on the road to Damascus. He was converted. Initiated into the ways of the world. And he liked it, his eyes gleaming with new-found insight and faith. He would evangelise, through his chalks, and make his fortune as he did so. He would even change his name: Tommy The Kid, Fastest Draw In The West.

Of course, his brothers at school threatened to beat him up unless he told them where he'd got the money, and demanded their cut. Their eyes gleamed as well when he told them and, the next day, a couple of them came along to watch.

The queue was not as long as Monday's, but Mark and Danny each had an empty jam jar, which they shook under the waiting noses. Some were gruff, others smiled and gave a donation.

'Hey,' said Danny, aged thirteen and with the eldest and canniest head, 'what we need's to hit 'em when they comes out. That's when they've got the money. It ain't no use when they're queueing.'

'It gets them interested.'

'We can't wait 'til it opens. That's school time.'

'Stuff school. We could make millions if we got 'em when they comes out. Millions'n trillions.'

'You're too far away down there Tommy. And the board's nearly all filled up. It's pretty rubbishy anyhow.'

'It's better'n you'd do, stupid.'

'Stupid you.'

'Shut it. Get this. Tommy can do the pavements tomorra. The girls can come down an'all.'

'They can't draw.'

'Nah, but they can dance or something.'

'Ha, that'll be a laugh.'

'They've got their chicken costumes from the school assembly.'

'Chickens don't dance.'

'Why not?'

'On Bugs Bunny they do.'

'I'll collect. Mark, you can do some gambols.'

'Why don't you?'

'Someone's got to collect.'

'You could do some break-dancing.'

'Yea, that'd be great. We could use mum's tape player.'

'Yes. We need some sound. That'd get 'em interested. Come on, we'll be late.'

'Who cares?'

All that day they thought of nothing else, the teachers barely noticing the more than usual reluctance to do any work. Tommy's maths book was covered with Supermen and Wonderwomen zapping Mysterons and his story about what he'd like for Christmas was an opportunity too good to be missed.

That night they roped in the two girls, Angie and Suzie, seven and five, and they practiced their acts until their fraught mother had finally had enough. There was very little room to practice in their small terraced council house. It was modern, with three bedrooms, but only one living room. If dad'd been there, they wouldn't've been able to do it, but he was in Winson Green for eighteen months.

Tommy, Mark and Danny shared a bed in one room, Angie and Suzie shared the other. Chattering away under the bedclothes, they could hear their mum busy downstairs doing the washing in her twin-tub.

The next morning they all trooped out, as usual without breakfast, the girls with their chicken suits and Danny with the portable tape player. Tommy chose a pavement slab at the head of the queue to chalk on and the girls danced up and down, clucking and singing a little chicken song, albeit shyly and quietly, between bouts of ear-piercing music and exhausting break-dancing as Danny and Mark flung and spun themselves about the roadside.

People started to clap. Danny went along with the jar when the girls were on. They called themselves "The Robinson Family Circus". This time, they stayed until the post office opened. As Danny had suspected, people coming out would drop in a lot more, occasionally a fifty pee, once they had their money. They didn't get into school until after ten, and Danny was hauled up before his headmaster. He explained how his mother was desperately ill and they'd had to wait for the chemist to open before they could come to school. The head, used to his stories, gave him a severe telling off.

Thursday was superb. It was pension day and the queue started at half-eight and stretched right along the shops. Danny had the idea of singing Christmas carols. They learnt snatches of "Away In A Manger" and "Good King When-I-Saw-Him-Last". Tommy drew a message on a piece of cardboard and they found some tinsel to put on their heads. Mark even had a candle he could hold as they sang. Angie had asked mum for some hankies someone had bought dad – she said they were a present for teacher – and she sold them along the queue for twenty pence each. Danny had thought of selling popcorn as well and had bought some at the sweet shop. He had also dreamt up better excuses and had forged five sick notes, two for flu, one for mumps, one for chicken-pox and one for malaria.

The queue was an unlikely place, given the poverty of nearly everyone on it, but most of them appreciated the side-show. Many were as badly off as the kids themselves; the single parents, pensioners, young unemployed, old men living on the verge of destitution. The better off customers came later or went to the post offices in town. However, neither the school nor the police appreciated it. The head of Danny's school was not convinced by the scrawls of unique spelling passed off as sick notes. They had been spotted and, he was warned, the family business would rapidly be squashed if it reared its head again.

Danny took the hint. He fingered his share of the twelve pounds they'd made that morning and, regretfully, decided their premature experiment in enterprise was, like most in the present economic climate, merely a day-dream. 'But,' he thought, 'what about the precinct in the school holidays?'

The Burges

WORKING THE PICTURES

'This one looks promising,' he thought, striding up the short path to the door. He gave the knocker three loud bangs. Confidence, even cheek, that was what you needed.

It was obviously a privately owned house. You could tell them straight away. Most of the houses on the council estate were strictly identical, faced in grey pebble-dashing, but this one had that thin sandstone laid carefully over the brickwork, as well as a new porch with a mock-gas courtesy lamp.

These were the best. People with a bit of money to spend, especially just before Christmas. It was nippy in the December evening, but not as cold down here in sea-warmed Plymouth as it was getting back in Coventry. He knocked again. A middle-aged man came to the door.

'Hi, I'm from the Coventry and Warwickshire Arts Students. We're selling pictures to raise funds for a new extension on our college. Here, look. These are done on genuine silk canvas. Look at that. Isn't that kingfisher pretty. And here's one of an eagle. This one's a genuine copper print.' He had the man's attention by now and watched as he relaxed, looked at the pictures and leant casually against his doorframe. As he mouthed his blag, Jimmy showed off his wares. He had a canvas bag over his shoulder, where he kept about ten pictures, eight meeds and two bigguns, all mass-produced prints, worth about ten pence each, under glass and cheap, gaudy wooden frames. The wood was so bad, he had to be very careful not to chip it or scrape any of the gold paint off.

'These are very expensive in the shops,' his blag continued. 'Most places you can't get them. Only in them exclusive art shops. These medium sized ones (never call them small!), they're eight ninety-nine in the shops and the bigguns are twenty-four ninety-nine. But we're offering a discount (never say cheap!), to help our funds.'

'Where' you from, did you say?'

'Coventry and Warwickshire Art students. We need money desperate for a new extension. It's a new art block. Painting an' all that.' In fact, he'd never been near the art college in his life, except once, when he fancied a girl student who'd been there. He was eighteen, unemployed, lived in a guesthouse and was doing the pictures to get a few readies before Christmas.

'We're really desperate for funds, you know, so we're offering them at a real discount. We're giving them away.'

'How much?'

'Six fifty for the mediums and twenty-one fifty for the bigguns.'

'That's still expensive.'

'We have to pay nearly that for them ourselves. We only make about a pound on each. But ain't they pretty. D'you have any kids? Here, they'll love this one.' He pulled a print of a leopard cub out of his bag. He knew they were tatty, but they looked better than they were. Straight out of his bag, they were shiny, smart and colourful. The fact that they quickly chipped and faded was no business of his. The prints were pretty good, really. Some of the Hans Christian Anderson's were real cute. It was just that they weren't worth the money he was asking.

'We pays five-fifty for the mediums to the manufacturer, and even then, he's doing us a favour.' It was all blag. All a con. Not a word of truth. Some sellers even went so far as to say they were from Shelter or Live Aid or some Art Aid or whatever. But that was too much for Jimmy. That wasn't right. Anyway, if you got caught saying that, you'd be right in it.

The man wanted to look at a couple under the hall light.

'Um,' he said eventually, 'how much d'you say?' knowing full well the price, but intimating to Jimmy to make a better offer. Jimmy knew to outpsyche him and stuck to it.

'I don't know,' the man said.

'It ain't worth us selling them for less. We'll never raise enough if we do. We're trying to raise money for handicapped students an' all.' Appeal to his sympathy. Make him feel a bastard for trying to haggle. But also make him feel you're the one being done. That was the secret. Do him, but let him feel he's done you.

'O.K. I'll take a kingfisher and an owl. How much's that?'

'Thanks very much. Thirteen quid.'

He disappeared for a couple of minutes, returning with two ten pound notes. Jimmy gave him his change.

'Would you like a big one as well?'

'No thanks.'

'O.K. Goodnight.'

'Goodnight.' And the door closed.

Jimmy stuffed the money into his pocket and ran down the path and up the road to a waiting car. Inside, the driver, who was the organiser, waited.

'Two meeds.' Jimmy handed over the seven quid cut for the driver.

'Get two more out the boot.'

Jimmy obeyed, then walked back to resume his walk up the street. He signalled two to his team-mate across the road. That was five to him and four to Jimmy in the hour since six o'clock. The next dozen or so doors were a dead loss. Everyone was interested, but none bought them. He had to judge when someone was just stringing him along. He had no time to waste. He had to make his money. So, if they didn't buy within ten minutes, he would get stroppy and call their bluff. Some felt obliged to buy, others didn't.

The next house was better. As soon as the door was opened, he knew he was on to a winner. A young, well-dressed woman with two young kids. She invited him in. Straight away, the price went up. Getting inside was worth a quid on a meed and a fiver on a biggun. She liked them and ordered four meeds. He had pushed the Andersons and a couple with Donald Duck and Mickey Mouse.

'D'you want a large one as well?'

'I've no space.'

'You must have.'

'Well,' she laughed, 'if you can find somewhere to hang it, I'll buy one.'

'Over there.'

'I want these two for there.'

'In the kiddies' bedroom?'

'These two.'

'In the hall?'

'I don't think so. You can look if you like.'

He went into the hall and, after a bit of thought, found an ideal spot between the living room door and the telephone.

'There,' he said, holding it up where it might go.

'It matches the paper.'

'It looks great. Real great. No kidding.'

'O.K. I'll take it.'

They went back to the living room and she wrote a cheque for sixty pounds. She'd agreed to pay sixty-five, but, out of the goodness of his heart, he had made it sixty. Sixty quid for a load of junk. Some people were so stupid, he couldn't believe it. He left the house, into the dark. It was getting late. They only knocked up until nine thirty and he'd had a good night already, so he went to the end of the street and sat on the road sign, waiting for his mate and for the car.

The car arrived within a few minutes of Mick. He and Jimmy piled in. There were five sellers altogether and the conversation bubbled in the cramped, sweaty Vauxhall. They'd all had a good night. None of them had blanked out.

They were driven to the bed and breakfast they were going to stay at and left their meagre belongings there, then filed out to do the pubs.

Sometimes a publican would let them set up a little display whilst they sat and drank. Others would let them go around touting. He might sell one or two at night, but it was very hit and miss and after a couple of pubs they usually gave up and decided to go on to a night club.

Jimmy, like all the sellers, was by now well high on blow. Some of them had even smoked a joint before going selling. It made them feel good, smiling at the world. But too much made you useless and Jimmy preferred to get the money in first. The take that night had been nearly seven hundred quid, between the five of them. The driver received over three hundred of that, for doing nothing except drive down and back and making sure they were O.K. He had to buy the pics and set them out in the bags as well, but buying them at only a quid each, he was making it hand over fist. And they'd be out again on Thursday/Friday. There was a lot of tax-free money in it and he'd heard of some team drivers banking nearly five thousand quid in one night. Some teams were bigger, mind. A whole minibus might go down and if they were good sellers and hit virgin prop, they could rake it in. Some nights everyone bought them.

But it was getting harder to find virgin prop now. The pictures had been going for at least fifteen years and so many teams went out on each shift, sometimes you'd be doing an estate another team had done only a couple of weeks before. Coventry was the national centre for it. Each shift saw eighty to a hundred teams out, of maybe a carload or a minibus full. So six or seven hundred kids must be going out on a shift. Either Monday to Tuesday or Thursday to Friday, setting off from a pub in town, or picked up from home about midday and then speeding up the motorway to Manchester, Wales, London, even Scotland. In fact, the market was getting so saturated that they needed to go further and further. It was time someone thought of another gimmick – teddy bears or something.

They entered the local nightclub and danced away the night, getting more stoned, then staggered back to the car and the guest house. They all missed breakfast, then coyly dribbed and drabbed out to a local pub before, in the late afternoon, starting on another estate. They quickly realised it had been done several months before, but long enough ago for there to be a few sales. Jimmy sold a pair of copper foil prints, which looked like lithographs, but, of course, were only hardboard.

The way you dressed was important. You had to look like students. Long hair was good. One bloke wore bright green trousers, pumps and a purple jacket. He had long, greasy hair and hadn't shaved for a week, but he cleaned up. He sold more than all the others put together. Nineteen and eight, if he could recall. They must have all taken pity on him.

They worked in pairs, one to each side of a street, with several pairs working an estate and the driver buzzing between them, keeping them stocked. Some drivers were good. One even had walkie-talkies for them. Most had been sellers who had then hired a car, until they could buy their own. There was so much money in it, every driver made a packet.

A few had been caught. The police usually kept an eye out. It was all illegal, and you could be done for fraud. Once, he'd been stopped and questioned, but he'd said he was only taking orders. They stopped him for a few minutes, then let him go. He had about forty quid in his pocket at the time. He always denied there were others, if he could, because one bloke had been sent down for eighteen months for conspiracy to defraud. That was a much bigger sentence. They had to watch that. In Bristol, the local T.V. did a programme on it and when they had gone round, people had started threatening to call the police, so now no one ever did Bristol.

The S.S. kept watch as well. He'd been caught last year and had had his benefit stopped. But he'd got back on it and was still selling pics. It was something he just watched out for. They never paid copyright to the artists either. Walt Disney would really screw them if they were caught.

It was an art. Conning was a fine art. You show people the pictures you think they'll go for. Once you're inside, you're made. You chat 'em up. You look for hints. If it's well furnished, if they've got lots of rings on, or nice clocks, then the price goes up. If they've got kids, you push the Andersons, or pets, you push the leopard cub and the birds. The kingfisher was the best seller by miles.

The first picture you sold paid your bed and breakfast, then the rest was easy money. You gave three fifty of each meed and fifteen quid of each biggun to the driver and kept the rest. So what you got was up to you. It was all in the blag, in the way you got them hooked. Sometimes you could really hit the jackpot. One big house he had gone to he had got a hundred and five quid for four bigguns.

Then there were the army bases. You had to get special permission and there were a lot of military police around, but they really went for them in a big way. But even they were getting over-done.

It wasn't as good as it used to be. He was thinking of giving it up, it was getting so hard now. He'd been at it since he was sixteen. Some were as young as twelve or thirteen. That was pretty bad. That was exploiting them. He didn't agree with that. But, as far as he was concerned, the driver might be doing him, but he was doing the customer, so he didn't give.

It was a good crack. A laugh. They all had a good time. They made easy money, got high on blow, had a night out.

It was like work to some teams, though. Wednesdays and the weekends, they would sleep it off, then be out again. He supposed it was better than doing nothing. Yea, it was a good crack, that was all. He'd been doing it for two years, but was getting fed up with it now. He'd stick it until Christmas, then jack it in. But that was life. Make what you can, how you can, when you can. Then move on.

POOL MEADOW

At Pool Meadow the queues wait in the sunshine and shade of the bus shelters. Every so often, a blue and cream bus throttles into life, its air-sealed doors clatter open and the driver behind his vandal-proof perspex screen issues tickets to the people boarding.

A couple of elderly women, pensioners who must catch their bus home before the rush hour, look around. Some young children swing and play catch around the shelter posts. The newspaper vendor can be heard shouting "City Fi. . . Nal!"

It is hot, burning hot, in the July afternoon. People don't want to bother with exertion. Young mothers in tight jeans and cotton tops look beautiful in the sultry, windless air. They glory in their youth and good looks.

A young couple of campers, with heavy backpacks over their deeply bronzed shoulders ask a bus inspector for some information. He looks very hot in his navy blue uniform of jacket, trousers, tie and hat and soon strolls back into the shade by the ticket office.

The two old ladies board their bus, which has finally come. The toddlers are called by their mother, as she searches her purse for the right change, a man runs across the tarmac to just catch the 32 and a number of pigeons settle by the clock on the roof of the café.

The Precinct

24

COUNCILLOR ARTHUR WAUGH, SENIOR

I had arranged to meet the man who was, in many ways, one of the fathers of the Council, in the lobby of the Council House. I pushed through the revolving doors into the lobby of the elegant Victorian building and saw him sitting opposite the reception desk. He greeted me, rose onto his walking stick and led me to the lift.

We went up a floor and walked through the corridors, past numerous numbered doors and through several swing doors, into the L-shaped room assigned to the committee chairmen. We sat and, after a few pleasantries, were served with tea in a solid silver tea service. We started to talk about crime in the city.

'It's become a great deal worse over the years,' Councillor Waugh said. 'Unemployment is the core. People with no money see theft as the only way out. It's like the increasing incidence of drug abuse. That is truly terrifying. They see it as easy currency. If you look at the crime figures, most new offenders are between eighteen and twenty-five.

'It's a deteriorating society we see around us. The police made an initial mistake when they employed the panda cars, instead of staying on the beat, with local bobbies who knew the area they patrolled. The very presence of a policeman on the beat is a deterrent.

'There is a tendency in the youth to want the pleasures they see around them, on the T.V., or that their parents have got. But they have no choice at all when they're on the dole. The contrast between the generations is much deeper now.'

'I think the old generation gap was between parents who'd had nothing and slaved for everything and their better-off, more educated children,' I interrupted, 'but now, it's between better-off parents and children who have nothing.'

'It's certainly true that the parents were lifted on a boom and that's what they wanted for their kids. Now that bubble has burst. I feel sorry for the kids today. I've got grandchildren who want jobs. Proper jobs, not like the Y.T.S. That's just cheap labour, with no real prospects and the young know that.

'Unemployment puts more stresses onto families. We've seen a lot of marriages breaking up and one-parent families are all too prevalent in Coventry. Women's liberation hasn't helped. It's upset the traditional roles in the family. Parental control has decreased. The media popularises promiscuity and ridicules parents and teachers. Family discipline is central. I'm an old-fashioned disciplinarian when it comes to

25

the schools as well.

'People at the very bottom end are worse off today, I think. Their education is bad, their ignorance is appalling.

'The Council's response has been to fund community projects, like the Jubilee Crescent youth club in Radford. That's used a great deal. They haven't enough nights in the week up there. Also, there are outward bound schemes, to compensate for the lack of adventure in people's lives these days. There's a real lack of ambition amongst people. But I feel so much frustration, that it's all just window-dressing, so long as there's so much unemployment. Kids these days demand independence earlier. They have higher expectations and better education. It's all fashions nowadays. Kids want to have the right hairstyles, dress with the fashions, and the media directs its attention at the eighteen to twenty-five year olds. So those most without are those most markedly deprived.

'The tower blocks were a disaster. They are awful for women with children and are much easier to vandalise. They've just added to the deterioration of the estates.

'I don't know the answer to vandalism. I wonder sometimes if it's the youngsters expressing themselves, all that spray-paint. You know, a release. Did you see that play on Coventry? "Risky City"? That was about the kids' frustration and depression. Everyone needs to feel pride, don't they. But today a lot of them can't have any ambition. Even when they try to succeed, it doesn't work. All that outlandish dressing's a statement that they've given up on trying.

'I think it's especially hard for black kids. They suffer from a lot of disenchantment. Their parents have high expectations of them, but the reality of the situation is different. It's hard for the Asian parents to fathom out what's going wrong. They have tended to think that qualifications were everything.

'Our new "Passport to Leisure" card, entitling all claimants to enjoy Council sports and leisure facilities freely or very cheaply, has been a tremendous success. It's things like that the unemployed need to keep them off the streets and out of trouble.

'I think all these gangs are around because none of them want to stand out as individuals. They want to be in a herd. Each one prompts the next to be a little more daring.

'In the schools as well, the attitude is often to look after the high-flyers and to ignore the bottom rung. So those down there feel abandoned in large classes, with little provision made for the slow learners. But we have tried positively to change that. The Minority Support Group Service offers a lot of help to ethnic minority children. That's been very positive.

'We need more special schools as well. We need to involve the slow learners, motivate them, give them some ambition. They don't have any

26

exams or letters after their names. All they can hope for is an unskilled job.

'The social services have been hopelessly stretched. We don't have enough home helps or nurses and now the health authority wants to close Paybody Hospital and sell Whitley Hospital to a housing association. I fear their elderly patients will be left for social services to pick up. There are too many elderly on their own as it is. They're going to suffer the most. They're living longer, but being taken out of hospitals and put back into their homes. It's just to cut the waiting lists, that's all.

'It's very distressing at times. Many of the elderly have lost a limb or are on a lot of drugs. Our home helps find it very distressing at times.

'There's a waiting list for our old people's homes and some never get in. Our home helps are very stretched, but we can't provide more, because we are afraid of being rate-capped.

'We aren't building any council houses now, for the same reason. We used to build two thousand a year in this city. All we can do now is modernisation, but that's very expensive as well. Seventeen thousand homes need improvement grants. There's simply not enough money. It'll take twenty-five years to do them all at the present rate.

'Selling council houses is greatly reducing the housing stock. People only buy the best. They tend to be the two and three bedroomed houses which go. They go for less than their market price. The waiting lists get longer. We are forced to sell a house for £6,000, when it costs nearly £20,000 to build a new one. For many tenants, it's cheaper to buy than to rent. The government has cut subsidies for housing as well. Out of a previous total stock of 28,000 homes, we're down three or four thousand. That's a considerable loss of revenue. And no building means no building jobs either.

'There has also been an attack on Council services such as catering, refuse collection, housing repairs and grass-cutting, by private firms. But the Council's workers are very efficient and so get the tenders.

'We have also lost a two pence rate from the abolished Metropolitan Council, which used to go to funding urban schemes. Urban Aid only funds projects for three or four years, so we find we can't finance on-going projects, only capital financing. That restricts our ability to finance worthy projects in the deprived areas of the city. There are no end of schemes worthy of support, but we have to decide on our priorities. It's terrible. It's the power of life and death. It's like a doctor deciding whether to turn off a life-support machine. That's how desperate it's become.'

The City centre

IN THIS CITY

In this city,
The father never had it so good,
With the highest wages in the country.

In this city,
The son, facing unemployment,
Has never been so disillusioned.

In this city,
Expectations were the greatest
And the shock of depression the hardest.

In this city,
Preoccupied with money,
We lost our culture and our identity.

In this city,
With its boom-town atmosphere,
We had no roots nor history.

In this city,
The question is not how much for life,
But how little for survival.

In this city,
Where boom led to self-confidence,
Crisis now promotes self-critique.

ON AN ISLAND

He knew it was a mistake. Even as he hobbled across the ring road to the central island, he knew he shouldn't. But he thought he'd be clever. Despite his ankle, which he'd badly sprained the day before, old habits died hard and he had treated the subway with his usual disdain.

It was five in the evening and the traffic was heavy, but never enough to cause a jam which would enable him to weave between the stopped cars. If there hadn't been a space in the traffic on the first side, he would probably have hobbled down the underpass and have been well on his way home by now.

There was a gap coming. He prepared himself, ready to spring across, but it was suddenly filled by two cars coming on from a side road. That was the trouble. This part of the ring road was three carriages wide and there was a filter road with a jam of cars on it, waiting to merge into the slightest let up in the main stream of vehicles.

The next hole was also filled. The next one disappeared as one car went exasperatingly slow, and he cursed it out loud as it chugged past, an old man at the wheel.

'Everyone over fifty should be banned from driving,' he remonstrated.

The next gap was filled by a driver swerving into another lane, without signalling.

'Useless women drivers,' he mumbled, 'they should all be banned as well. All of them.' But, as the car went past, it turned out to be a young man with long hair.

'Get your hair cut,' he shouted.

He stared at his watch. 'This is ridiculous.' Then, shouting at the next car, 'This is ridiculous! Ten minutes I've been here.'

Suddenly, there was another gap. But not big enough, with his bad ankle. It was filled from the filter road as it was. A decrepit removal lorry stormed past, blasting fumes into his face and nearly knocking him over in its speed and closeness to him.

To his right, the speeding road descended to an underpass fitted with a row of neon strip lights. Concrete was everywhere, hemming him in and chanelling the cars along strict conduits of husting energy. Tin cans jostled from lane to lane, indicators barely flashing, sharp-witted and nearly-careless drivers seeking the fastest moving lane in an effort to get home a few seconds earlier. The billowing, sucking wind buffetted him on his narrow sanctuary. He looked lost.

It was unpleasant. It was scarey. One mistake by a thirty-eight ton artic, and it would leave tyre marks all over him. He felt the claustrophobia of futility. His job and general prospects came into his mind as he started to day-dream. His lack of prospects hemmed him in. Life without a future is the most suffocating feeling of all. The claustrophobia of suicide. He even contemplated, in his dazed, staring day dream, swaying on his thin haven, just closing his eyes and walking into the flow. To let himself be whisked along upon the gentleness of oblivion.

This inner ring road, a planner's paper dream, had become a Berlin Wall between the city's centre and its people.

The old, cramped streets, unhealthy, but at least with character and humanity, had been replaced with a concrete precinct of identical shops, with car parks meandering over the roofs and paved pedestrian areas. The old alone remembered, always missing what had been.

The ring road encircled the heart of the city, accessible only via subways and underpasses. A heart dead, except when it was filled with the soul of its people breathing life into it as the day awoke.

He decided to sit down and roll himself a cigarette. There was no sign of the traffic slackening and it would take the weight off his aching ankle. Near there, the other way, he had witnessed a Japanese woman having her bag snatched in a subway. He'd passed her as she was going into it, then heard a scream and saw a young man run off the other way with her bag. All he could do was comfort her, but her handbag was gone, with her passport and traveller's cheques. He'd called the police and given her his phone number, in case she needed help. What else could he have done? Just show her that there were still some people left who cared.

An Asian doctor had been stabbed a few years back outside a baked potato take-away near his house one night. A young woman had been killed less than a hundred yards from the house and the supermarket across the road had been burgled several times. A black lad had been found drowned in a river, suffering from the effects of glue and an old lady had been beaten up and raped by a couple of boys in her home.

'I'll have to bring my bed next time.'

He thought about his dinner which would be waiting for him at home, and his young wife, wondering where he was.

'Perhaps they'll send out a search party.'

By now, his watch had gained another twenty minutes. There was another gap, again filled. The traffic slowed right down as more and more vehicles crowded onto the road, but not enough for him to nip through, and then gathered speed again. He tried to hold his hand up and act the traffic cop, but it was useless. He was nearly run over. He turned around and thought about going back again, but his retreat was as suicidally busy as his advance. He even thought about walking along the island to find a better spot, but one way was the tunnel and the other way the island ended abruptly.

He looked around. This bit of the ring road was slightly below the level of the surrounding land.

'Faceless, totally faceless,' he muttered. 'Just like all these cars. Sameness. Identical people inside them as well. All rushing, none of them giving a damn about *me*.' He was getting desperate. His ankle was throbbing and he was cursing every car that went by. His watch read five to six.

Over the tops of the buildings around him, he could see a high crane still swinging in its work.

'Another monstrosity going up,' he thought. People talked about a new city rising from the ashes, but so much good in the old had gone as well. The funny thing was, that as the boom went on, most people had accepted the benefits were worth the destruction. But now, with the new, the present, of unemployment and cuts, there was a lot of regret about what they had lost.

Indicators flashed their intentions, large signs hung threateningly overhead, imposing their rigid lanes and instructions upon the drivers, overpasses merged into underpasses, the sky became underground, large white arrows, hatched lines and cat's eyes ordered, separated and categorised.

He stared up at the monstrous steel girder looming overhead, bearing the massive green road signs and those little white arrows ordering drivers into line and lane. It dominated him. Its black shadow lengthening rapidly in the evening sun, with its flimsy, vulnerable ladders welded to each huge leg.

'They could dangle a rope ladder down from there,' he thought. 'Pass me food parcels and hot drinks. Perhaps a sleeping bag.'

Society was breaking up, like the surface of the road. Cracking under the strain, but with no one left to repair the human damage. Home helps were going, as were teachers, social workers and community workers. Charities and special units, like the Drugs Team, were being asked to fill the gaps in homelessness, provision for mental illness, the elderly, or in any other social service. Hospital wards were closing, the ambulance service had been moved away, and crime was violently increasing. There was a growing black economy of the unemployed, seeking ways of surviving, as illegality replaced decent social benefits and adequately paid jobs. Health and safety in many factories was being taken with a pinch of salt. House building by the council had ground to a total stop, direct repairs were under assault and homelessness was rising.

There was despair out there in the city. The concrete walls and ring roads no longer meant modernity, they meant facelessness and lack of caring. They meant thousands of people and their families who thought the world had forgotten them and whose existence was day-to-day, with no sign of relief.

It was getting cold and getting dark. He zipped his jacket and tried to walk up and down to keep warm. His ankle was aching terribly. Quarter past six. Another gap, but no, not enough. He'd be sausage meat half way across. He waved at a passer-by on the far side, trying to explain his plight in sign language, but spelling "helicopter" proved too difficult and the man walked off.

Perhaps, he thought, they could string a rope over and he could swing across, hand over hand. Tunnelling would take too long. His dinner would be completely spoilt. Anger turned to despair, then back to anger. He cursed his isolation. He screamed and ranted against it. He shouted at every vehicle going past and demanded to be let off. If they'd been going slow enough, he would have booted them all as well, or ripped their wing mirrors off – anything to express his total frustration.

And there we must leave him, stuck on his island, between two endless streams of cars, because he still hasn't found a way to escape.

Hertford Precinct

FROM PILLAR TO POST

Gail was not afraid of mice, which was just as well.

She lived in a bedsit on the ground floor of a terraced house in St Nicholas Street, Radford. The landlord, a building contractor, who had a number of properties in the city, had heard that a housing association was buying the other properties in the row and doing them up. "Ah," he thought, "just the job. I'll get a good price for it. No need to do any repairs, the worse a state it's in, the more likely they'll buy it." And so he hadn't done any repairs. Nothing for years.

When Gail had moved in last year, the front door had been loose and the lock on her room had been forced. The room itself was damp and the furniture, old already, showed signs of having been thrown about. The landlord had promised to fix everything, but, of course, had not.

Since then, one Friday, when the house had been empty, someone had broken in the front door and systematically stolen everything of any value in all the rooms, from top to bottom. Most of them had been out cashing their giros at the time. None in the house had jobs. In fact, that was the way the landlord liked it. He would get them to sign a form so the D.H.S.S. would pay the rent direct to him. He got his money regularly and assuredly and could charge a higher amount than many young workers would have been prepared to pay.

Gail had her radio and a bracelet her mother had bought her stolen. She had nothing else of any value. No television, no record player, no decent clothes or good shoes or other jewellery. Since then, the front door had been hanging off its hinges and her own door needed no key to open it, just a good shove. Also, all the meters had been raided and the landlord, fed up because it had happened a number of times before, refused to have them fixed. So she had had lighting, but no heating or hot water and couldn't use the decrepit cooker sulking in the corner by the window. This had been during January and February. She would go out as much as she could, to friends, a café, or the library, but she couldn't afford to sit around drinking tea. In the flat, she would make herself a sandwich and sit in her chair with a blanket around her, or go to bed.

It had been one evening, when she was sitting in her chair eating a cheese sandwich under the dull glow of the 60 watt bulb, that she first noticed Nibbles. She had been sniffing around the bottom of the blanket, eating the crumbs dropping from the sandwich. Gail had watched her quietly feeding, oblivious to any danger, then scamper back under the bed. At first, the mouse had been christened Maurice, but she had come the next time with four tiny mice behind her.

Gail had discovered the minute crack in the skirting board they would emerge from and became accustomed to the scratching which went on within the wall. At times, she would also see them come out as she lay in bed and even climb up onto the foot of the bed, in their search for food.

The landlord had finally been threatened by one of the tenants upstairs with the law and had had the meters fixed. Gail still had to be careful with the one-bar fire, but it made a great difference to the room and she could also keep the small geyser on for hot water.

It had been soon afterwards that she had started to hear strange new sounds at night. It was like a short pitter-patter, then a "whoo, whoo" sound, like a low whistle. It worried Gail a lot. It might be a rat. The thought of one of them terrified her. She'd seen a dead one in the back yard one morning, as big as a cat.

She was only twenty. She had lived in Coventry since she was two, her parents moving from the Rhondda in Wales. She was one of seven. But then her parents had divorced, her mum had gone back to Wales and they had all stayed with their dad, who had remarried. Their step-mother had had a family of her own, older than them, and she had always treated them quite differently to her own. Their house, large as it had been, had been overcrowded.

Then her father had left and their step-mother had taken in another man, so neither of the adults bringing her up had been her real parents.

She loved her father, who had always been honest with her and showed her love in return, but loathed her step-mother and her man, who was just ignorant and stupid. He worked in a car factory on the line doing something or other, she didn't care.

She heard the pitter-patter again, followed by the two low whistles, then again, as it repeated itself several times. She rose quietly, tip-toed to the light switch and turned on the light. The noise stopped, a mouse darted under the bed, but otherwise nothing. She looked around. There was no sign of other life at all. She decided to make herself a cup of tea, so turned a ring on and filled a saucepan with water.

School had been hell for her. She had only done about three years in all at secondary school. The second year, she had been in and out of hospital and, in the fourth, she had been so fed up with it, seeing no point, knowing what sort of life she would be leaving school for anyway, that she skivved most of it. But then her brother had come home from the army and he had made her study for her exams. In the end, although she had done very little work and only sat the exams for the sake of it, she had achieved six C.S.E. Grade 1s.

Since then, she had done a few jobs, but wanted to become a nursery nurse, anything to get a bit of money. She adored kids, loved them. Her older sister had been the same. It had taken her three years to get a job, during which time she had been in a series of useless Y.O.P. courses which had led her nowhere at all.

The water was boiling now, so she put a teabag in her mug and poured it in, added some milk and four spoons of sugar, then fished out the soggy bag and dumped it in the bin.

The room was about the size of the back living room you'd find in most old terraced houses. It had a cooker, sink, bed, chair and wardrobe. But even that she found hard to keep tidy. Looking after herself had always proved a problem. She was overweight and would get horrible depressions which would last for weeks.

She had been taken into care when she was fifteen. She had become pregnant, which had made her relationship with her step-mother even worse, until one day they had had a row and she had pushed her step-mother right across the kitchen. She was a bag. But Gail had a temper on her. She would get emotional too easily and, although her step-mother was sixteen stone, she had gone right across the room. So Social Services had taken her into care. After going to court for them to take out a care order, she'd ended up in Stoke House. When her daughter had been born, she had been fostered. She would be five by now. Gail had never seen her since the birth. And now she was pregnant again.

She put on the bar fire and sat in the chair. She didn't have a watch, but guessed it was about midnight. She thought of turning on the radio, a new one her real mum had given her for Christmas. Mercia Sound permeated the room, "Magic at Midnight" love melodies drooling over the furniture.

Stoke House had been fun. They had enjoyed quite a lot of freedom, though they had needed to be in by nine-thirty. It had been a big place, with four blocks when she had stayed there, A, B, C and D, with eight kids in each unit, three of them "open" where you could go in and out, to school or work, but one secure. That had been some place. Each bedroom had seemed a cell, with a heavy door, locked every night. The window in each room had been only a narrow slit and all the furniture had been nailed to the floor. The kids had left their clothes outside their rooms in wardrobes and hadn't been allowed shoe laces or belts. The floors had been bare. Someone had hanged himself once. The kids in there had never been let out. They had gone to school in there, eaten their meals there and had used a hall for playing sports in the afternoons. Most of them had developed histories of shop-lifting, violence or truancy, or all three together. Some had become grateful for the security, but others had resented it and thought it was the authority's fault they had ended up in there. So they had worked a points system, to encourage the kids to help out and be well behaved. If they had earned enough points, they were able to watch the T.V. They had made their own light meals, although all the main meals had been cooked for them.

Gail had lived in one of the open units. The youngest kid there had been twelve. They had received a few pounds a week pocket money and had gone on holiday together to the Isle of Wight. Whilst there, she had worked on a petty, stupid Y.T.S. course, which had only been twenty-five pounds a week. Cheap labour. Then she had worked in a nursery as an assistant for six months. She'd enjoyed that. It was funny how all the girls in the unit had wanted kids, or to work with kids. Also, many of the staff had been in care themselves when kids. There was some sort of affinity. Kids had no expectations of her, no preconceptions. They didn't put her in a box with a label on. She felt confident with them. She could be herself.

When she had been taken into care, she had been assessed for six weeks, during which time she had seen a psychiatrist. The trouble with care was it had made them too dependent on others. She felt they had all been spoilt. They had had it all laid on for them. It had been such a contrast to her home. There, she had been given no money and no clothes. She'd never had that much pocket money in her life, though it still wasn't that much. It had felt nice. It had seemed caring and she had needed that. But when she had tried to make it in the big world, it had really hit her and she had found it impossible to cope.

She finished her tea and decided to turn off the light and radio and wait for the noise to start again. She settled into the dark of the chair and let her mind wander. She wasn't tired. She didn't sleep very well as it was and often stayed in bed reading a novel.

After a year or so at Stoke House, she had been moved to Wisteria Lodge. She had been there for eighteen months. She had found herself a job working in a toy factory, sewing up every furry animal you could imagine, from tiny pram toys to enormous rabbits and teddies as big as she was. She would come home to the Lodge, have her tea, then go down and help in the handicapped unit there. That had been closed since. A pity, she thought, as she had enjoyed that as well.

At the Lodge, they had been encouraged to take more decisions and have more independence. It had been more relaxed and they had been left more to themselves. They had gone over to the Memorial Park to play football, where she had usually ended up as the goalie. She had never known why, as whenever the ball had come anywhere near her, she had run a mile.

Then she had lost her job. The other girl had started throwing some soft hedgehogs around. She had thrown one back. They had been marched up to the manager's office and been sacked on the spot. Still, it had been a rubbish job, boring and low paid. And they had picked on her there, because she was overweight.

37

After leaving the Lodge, she had visited her mum in Cwmbran for a few weeks, then ended up in Verecroft, another house for teenagers. There it had been stricter. They had had rotas and had been strict about no messing about. Then, one day, on her eighteenth birthday, they had gone out to the pub to celebrate and, when she had come back, she had become involved in a fight. She had a terrible temper on her. After that, she had been sent up to another Richmond Fellowship unit in Liverpool, then brought back again.

She had been there until last September, when she had moved into a bedsit on her own. She hadn't been able to cope and the landlord had thrown her out onto the street. Then she had tried to live with her sister, but her boyfriend hadn't liked it. Her only choice had been the Cyrenians and she had stayed at their women's hostel for three weeks. They had helped her sort out the D.H.S.S., because she had faced so much trouble with them. They had helped her talk about the baby she was expecting and what she would do and had helped her to get on the Council waiting list. Then she had found this place. A friend had been moving out, so she had moved in.

The noise suddenly started again. A scratching sort of pitter-patter, a "whoo-whoo", repeated several times, then quiet. She waited for it to start again. It did. It was from near the sink. Pitter-patter, whoo-whoo, pitter-patter, whoo-whoo. She quietly rose and reached for the switch. When the light came on, there was a mouse, running along the top of the hot geyser with a pitter-patter, stopping every few steps to blow its paws with a little "whoo-whoo", before it scampered down a hole by the sink.

Job hunting

KAY

Kay.
I pull the dirty sheets from the cot
And hurl them on the pile of washing
By the door of the room the three of us sleep in,
Add a baby-grow and a blanket,
Sick-covered,
And my spattered nightie,
Reminiscences of a sleepless night.
I pick up yesterday's tiny vests and trousers,
A jumper, a soiled nappy,
Then bundling the collection,
Hold my breath,
Pick them up and carry them downstairs.

Kay.
I am Kay.
I am black,
I am a woman,
I am eighteen,
I am a vegetarian,
I have a telly with a slot for fifty pees.
I have no washing machine,
So must soak my things in bowls,
Then move them from bucket to bucket,
To squeeze and swirl and scrub and shake
And strangle the clothes dry,
From sink to drainer to clothes horse,
To hang dripping all this day and the next.

I am Kay.
I . . .
I am . . .

Yes,
I'm sure,
I am Kay.

I am the mother of Daniel, one and a half,
I am the mother of Simeon, eight months,
Who is so sick I must wash his bed each morning,
And so many sets of clothes.

I want my own,
I want my kids to grow with me,
To make up for the lack in my life,
For the frustration of school,
For no support from my mum,
For all the hand-me-downs
And second-hand beds and carpets,
For the years on social,
For the damp and cold.
I want them to have what I hadn't,
Even if it's just a new pair of shoes,
Or toys for Christmas.

I am Kay,
I am Rastafari,
I am independent,
I am a smoker of herbs,
Natural weed to succour the natural me,
To bring understanding and wisdom,
To allow the perfection of thought,
To make me happy,
To conquer challenges,
To see me through my trials
And bring me to me.

I need to find the buried me,
To shake off the rhythm of suppression,
To break from passing nothingness
And lay my claim to reality.

Life, drowning me in daily chores,
Sucks me into existence,
And simultaneously engulfs me
In a dream.
My thought and being tick past,
Without me knowing or witnessing,
Nor particularly caring.
Reality comes and reality goes,
Leaving me in a dream world,
From which I cannot awake,
To find it has passed me by.

People on the telly
Talk of missiles and defence and diplomacy,
The future of this great nation of ours,
But let me tell you of my future,
How little this nation means to me,
How absurd that greatness seems,
In the post office queue on Monday morning,
Feeding my kids on beans and chips,
Washing nappies by hand in my sink.

There is no time for me,
No ecstatic words,
No triumphant marches,
No trumpet voluntary,
No compassion, no thought,
No memory.

Yes,
I am the past without recall,
Which lives only to curse the future,
To praise the passing of time
And to dream of life.
I need time, but time does not need me;
I want to know what life is,

I want a weekend away from the kids,
I want steak one Sunday instead of chicken,
I want to ride to the pictures in a taxi,
I want to see the Blackpool lights,
I want to take my kids to the sea,
I want to breathe the cold mountain air,
Just once, just once.

I am Kay.
I am the timeless, most in need of time,
To learn what resonance life has;
I am the orator most in need of words,
To rant and scream about my plight;
I am the artist most in need of oils,
To slap and splash my pain before your eyes;
I am the poet most in need of hyperbole,
To describe the hopelessness of poverty;
I am the warrior most in need of a spear,
To cut and thrust through unconcern;
I am the boxer most in need of a fist,
To stamp upon a table and demand release.

I am Kay,
And I must fix the plug in the front room,
I must see to the damp in the bedroom,
I must prepare the dinner,
I must soak these clothes,
I must nip to the shops,
I must vacuum,
I must get to a phone
To ask about my laundry grant.

I am Kay,
I must not forget.

The Council House

44

GLUE SNIFFING

It was about two o'clock on a cold Wednesday afternoon in January. The frost caking the grass along the bank of the Sowe scrunched under the bodies of Sandie, Phil and James as they started to hallucinate.

Sandie pulled another freezer bag from a pocket of her jacket and unscrewed the top of the tin of glue before pouring some into the bottom of the bag. She grasped the neck of the bag with her fist and pushed a hole into it with her finger, then breathed in the glue vapours with several deep breaths.

It was her third bag. Two bags made her cheerful, usually making her cares evaporate and making the grass, the shrubs, and the trees smile back at her. The third would send her crazy. James had taken two, but that would be his lot. He always stayed in control.

As she sat on the ground, unaware of the cold, she stared at the small river running a few yards in front of her feet. Behind her was a small bank, topped with bushes which, although bare of leaves, still offered a screen for them. Across the river, the bank rose sharply to an old scrap yard.

The third bag was taking its effect. Her eyes dilated. She wanted to get up, but found it hard to coordinate her limbs. She fell and crawled and rolled over, down the bank.

'I want to go into the biggest shop in town, the biggest, and put on a fur coat. Just put it on and walk out. I do.'

Her thoughts swirled, betraying her. Her jelly limbs kept bending when asked to support her. She tried to rise, gave up, and the world rolled over and over again.

She had stolen the money for the glue from her mother's purse. She always stole. She had to. She lied to everyone. She stole from shops and friends. She had lied about her nan being ill to get money for medicines. She had even taken twenty pounds from nan's jar. She didn't care. When she was high, she felt so good, nothing could go wrong. She used to go into Woolly's and stuff handfuls of sweets into her pockets. She would go into shoe shops and walk out in a new pair of shoes, leaving her old ones on the rack. She would steal face lotions and lipsticks and make-up that she never used. She had a whole wardrobe full of them and used to tell her mum they were presents from friends. She didn't care a damn.

She began to crave for Phil to make love to her. She staggered towards him and tried to kiss him, then began to undress. She threw off her jacket. Phil tried to push her away, telling her she had had too much, but she still came on, trying to get her jumper over her head. She failed, so gave it up and tried to reach up behind her back to undo her bra.

'Make love to me, Phil,' she said. She could barely focus on him and didn't care what she did or said. She was feeling breathless and felt an intense pain in her chest.

James came over. 'Stop it,' he said.

'I don't care. I want him to make love to me.'

'You've had too much.' He pulled her hands down.

'Leave me alone. I want to. Phil wants to, don't you Phil?'

'No, Sandie, you don't mean it.'

'Bastard.'

'You've had too much.'

'Give me some more. I'll show you, bastard. F... you, bastard.'

'No.'

'F... off.' She pulled out another bag and unsteadily poured some more glue into it. Her mouth had several sores around it. She staggered around, tried to climb the bank, but slid down again. Her eyes couldn't focus and the trees started to move and growl at her. Phil was staggering around, stripping off as well. He was shouting about something.

Then she saw them. About ten people lying about the grass, naked, making love. Then they got up and she saw they all had guns. They were running towards her. Their eyes were on fire. Their bodies were greens and blues. They were after her. She had to escape, flee. The river was the only way. She must cross it. She could. She saw some stepping stones, the water was safe, she knew it was safe. They were firing their guns. They were screaming that they were going to cut her up and kill her. They had dogs with them, huge, black mastiffs, barking violently. She had to escape.

James tried to stop her, but too late. She fell into the river. James jumped in after her. She was completely submerged as he grabbed her, then pulled her up screaming about guns and dogs and escape, unaware of where she was.

An hour or so later, some passers-by saw her body lying on the bank. James and Phil had disappeared. They could smell the glue on her clothes and saw the discarded bags nearby. Sandie was half-naked and soaking wet, hardly breathing and going blue in the cold. They wrapped her in her jacket and one ran off to call an ambulance.

POSTSCRIPT

'What happened in the hospital?'

'They said I vomited all the time. They said I nearly died.'

'What was your mum's reaction?'

'It nearly killed her. She said I was vomiting a lot and was pale and weak. She had no idea I was on it. She never thought it would happen to me. We lived in a nice house in a good area. We were never badly off, so she never thought I would. She had wondered where all her money was going, but she never thought it was for glue.'

'How did you get off it?'

'It was hard. I never went to any classes or anything. I had to do it myself. Mum stopped all my pocket money. My brothers and sisters never lent me anything. My friends at school never did either. They never gave me a penny. I was desperate. I used to go into the hardware shops and try to steal it, but they all knew me and wouldn't even sell me any. I used to steal to get money. Then I would abuse the police. I was put on two year probation for stealing a load of Brut and perfumes from Boots. I'd go into Marks and just open a sandwich up and eat it there, or a cake or biscuits, anything. I didn't care. I got terrible cramps and cravings when I came off it. My stomach ached terrible. I had terrible headaches. I'd walk around and couldn't sleep. I'd tried to get my friends to get me glue, because all the shopkeepers knew me. I'd walk all over the city trying to get it.'

'What effect did it have on you?'

'It was destroying my brain. It was doing it in. I was hallucinating. One lad tripped in a tower block. He thought people were after him and he jumped off the balcony and was killed. That's what it can do to you. My breath stank. I never ate anything. I used to have terrible dreams.

47

Once, I dreamt I was being stabbed and, when I woke up, I found I'd got a bit of broken mirror and really jabbed myself with it. My side was all cut open.'

'What were the trips like?'

'Always bad. Always. It was always something terrible. I got paranoid and panicky. It was awful.'

'Why did you do it then?'

'My mates were on it, so I wanted to do it as well. It was the fashion. Everyone was doing it. Like, it's something else now. It looked good. I felt good. I enjoyed it as well. It was the boredom. I wanted to be like my mates. I wanted to steal. I wanted to abuse the police. When you're on it, you don't give a damn about anything, not even your family. It destroys you and everything around you. It really does.'

Priory Row

PLAYING TABLE TENNIS

'My serve, Dave.'

Dave was not a good table tennis player. But that wasn't the point.

'One, love.'

The object of the game had nothing to do with the little white ping pong ball that was smashed and sliced to every corner of the hall. It was to do with the two people sitting on a nearby table, waiting to play next.

'Two, love.'

You see, they were girls, and the one thing Dave couldn't stand was show-off girls who had to pretend they were as good as the lads.

'Three, love.'

They were so useless, it was untrue and he wasn't going to hang around whilst they played their stupid little pansy game.

'Four, love.'

In fact, if the girls ever *did* get to the table, the main object of all the lads' behaviour became to ridicule them as much as possible.

'Five, love; love, five. Your serve, Dave.'

'Love, six.'

'Love, seven.'

'That don't count.'

'It bounced twice, Dave, you pillock.'

Dave tried one of his special, high-lobbed, backspin smash serves.

'Love, eight.'

Right, he thought, time to stop messing and get down to business. Baz had scored his last point. Another smash serve.

'Love, nine. Straighten the net, Dave.'

A subtle drop serve. A return. Another smash.

'Sorry Paula. Love, ten; ten, love.' But Dave had discovered a new sport: deliberately aiming his smashes at the girls.

'Ow!'

'Eleven, love.'

'Get lost Dave.'

'Twelve, love.'

'If you do that again, I'll shove it down your throat.'

'Thirteen, love.'

'Ha, missed.'

49

'Fourteen, love.'

But, reflected Dave, this was not the right tactic, since the object was to stay on the table as long as possible. Baz admonished him as well for messing around. So he returned to the serious competition.

'Fifteen, love; love, fifteen.'

One of the girls was his – Claire. They were going steady. They'd been going steady for a week now. Once out to the flicks and once down the chippy and back, before going to bed together. But she was a nice girl, not like Susanna.

'Love, sixteen. Come on Dave, concentrate.'

'Get knotted, prat features.'

Nah, Susanna'd been a right slag, all tarted up, everything. He'd only wanted one thing from her, but when he'd got it, she was just too much of an embarrassment to him.

'Love, seventeen. Jesus Dave.'

She must've been thirty if she was a day. She drank like a fish and had a terrible laugh, a high-pitched titter, on and on and on. Ugh! And then she'd been sick all over the floor and fainted, showing off her knickers. That'd done it. All the lads were making fun of her, saying what they'd do to her. She made him puke.

'Love, eighteen.'

The girls began to giggle at him and echoed the score. Dave turned red. The next ball was slammed at them.

'Love, nineteen.'

'Love, nineteen,' they repeated, loudly. Dave's response, knowing he could never win the game now, was to play the fool. The next return bounced off the ceiling.

'Love, twenty; twenty, love.'

'Love, twenty,' came the mockery. 'Will he score at all?' Claire laughed.

Her enquiry was answered when the next serve, a dolly-drop, bounced half a dozen times on Dave's side of the net before he had realised what had happened. It was greeted with guffaws and applause from the whole gang of lads as well as the two girls.

'At least we ain't as useless as that,' Paula said. 'Come on, it's our turn, you've had five games already.'

'Not likely.'

'Go on Dave,' said Barry. 'I ain't playing with you again.'

Dave threw his bat across the hall, so Paula had to get it, then hid the other bat behind him, refusing to let Claire have it. Then, tired of that, he threw it to Baz, who threw it back, with Claire a piggy-in-the-middle, until she managed to catch it. His next strategy was to sit on the table, whilst they tried to play around him. He caught the ball and squashed it with a loud click.

The girls were only saved by Barry suggesting they get out the cricket bat and practice their Botham impressions. They waltzed off, leaving the girls to get another ball.

The youth club hall was full of activity as the paid leader, Baljit, involved the teenagers and tried to keep order. A game of pool was going on in another corner, a ghetto blaster rocked out Frankie Goes To Hollywood and the dulcet tones of Cliff hammering his drum kit emanated from the lounge.

Baljit, remembering the ceiling tiles they'd had to replace after the last time, refused their request to relive the great Headingley Test. They drifted back to wait for a turn at the pool. The girls, meanwhile, were well into their game.

'You see,' Dave thought to himself, 'there are girls and there are girls. Susanna was a tart. But Claire, she's pretty O.K., a real nice girl. That don't mean I should treat her with respect. Oh, no. All girls want to be given a rough time. That's what they want. If you go easy on them, they leave you.'

Like all the lads, he longed for a steady relationship. Not many of them had one and usually, when they got a girl, it ended after a few months. Nice girls wanted blokes with money. A steady job, that was what he needed. Not much chance of one though. It got to him. No job. No money. So he couldn't go out. Claire wanted to see Ah Ha at the NEC, but he couldn't afford that. She wasn't so bad. She knew the score a bit. She'd even offered to pay. There was no way he would let her. No way. No girl was going to keep him, no way. He didn't even like going dutch. He only allowed that as a last resort. He'd even borrow from one of his mates before going dutch. Girls shouldn't expect to pay and he didn't want anything to do with one who did. He disliked those libby women. They were too stroppy, too clever-clever. They scared him and kept on about equality and sexism. It got so as you couldn't say anything. He didn't want none of that. That was for all them lesbians and poofters. Ugh! They really gave him the willies. He wanted to smash their faces in. They scared him and all. A bloke chatting him up! He might put his hand on his knee. Ugh! He felt sick. "He might even try to kiss me," he thought. He'd beat the poofter's head in, pulverise the bastard. Baljit had said it was just the same as a girl felt when a bloke came up and pestered her. But it wasn't the same at all. Girls accepted it and wanted it, deep down. They liked being chatted up, they liked to flirt. It was all part of the game. Anyway, sometimes girls chatted him up and he didn't mind that, so long as, when he'd decided to ask them out, they accepted he was the boss. In fact, he felt good when a girl chatted him up. It gave him control. It took the pressure off him. He hated coming on strong, then being told to shove off. Hide your feelings, don't take nothing serious, that way it don't matter which way it goes.

He was careful not to show too much affection towards Claire. He'd largely ignored her tonight. He was keen on her, he bought her a few things, some Maltesers, a packet of chips, things like that, but when it came to the youth club, he was there with the other lads, not her. He hadn't asked her to come and wished she hadn't. The club was theirs, not for the girls. That was why he gave them such a hard time. Like pubs. Girls shouldn't ever go into pubs without fellas. It wasn't right. He hated girls in a group on their own in a pub and they should never ever be seen in a bar. Only slags went into bars. Women should never go out without men anyway.

He and Baljit used to argue about his attitudes. Claire's sister, Paula was like that. None of them could get away with anything with her. Once, he'd said girls liked a hard time and she'd heard. She'd been furious. She said it wasn't true. But she was talking crap. Sure, he didn't believe in beating women up, not in public anyway, he chuckled. His dad had thumped his mum and he hated that. He loathed their rows. But his mum accepted it, that's what got to him. She took it as normal and only thought it would be serious if dad broke her arm or something. Also, his sister saw all that and now she believed it was normal as well. She thought that was all there was. For her it was better to have a man, any man, than no man at all. She accepted it as something that just happened as natural as the night. She'd even told him that "Girls can't live without men".

Paula had been angry at him for that. She was into all that equality and freedom and respect and against sexism. But you should see her fella. A macho hulk if ever you saw. Blonde, six foot, all muscles. She was all talk. Girls love to be dominated. They expect it and want it. It was instinct, in-bred.

He looked at Claire and Paula. They were giggling away, playing like a couple of right wimpy women. Why can't girls do *anything* properly? Why do men have to do everything for them, *everything*? Even the best cooks were men. Ugh, the way they pathetically patted the ball over the net.

It was their turn to play pool. Barry collected the balls. Dave tossed a coin. He decided to break and cracked into the pack with venom. A striped ball pocketed itself. He pocketed another, then missed.

It was true, that was the point. Girls do stay with blokes who are bastards to them. They seemed to love it. He'd tried being nice, talking, caring, being thoughtful, but he'd become a friend, not a lover. It hadn't come over sexy enough for them. It wasn't manly enough. You see, it wasn't all men's fault. Women play to the stereotype men have of them and men do the same. Women want macho men, they love it, they know where they are then. So men turn on the style. They lark about, they buy flash cars, buy all the drinks, they treat their women to everything. Women like flashy men, it turns them on, so you've got to be flashy to get them. Then they all think they know what blokes want. They think a bloke wants a girl who just sits there, looking pretty. Or who's fun – in other words, giggly and stupid. She thinks he wants her in lipstick and high-heels and doesn't want her to talk seriously about anything. She thinks she has to be all light and fluffy. She's right. She does. But it wasn't men's fault if they thought like that. If they want fellas, they've got to look like the blokes want them to. Anyway, they're worse than the blokes. They hate looking like tarts, or like students.

His go again, and he aimed a long pot, which missed, but blocked the pocket. That was half the game – blocking the pockets. And it suited his mood. The girls had finished their game and were now back to sitting on the tables. Two other girls had joined them. That was all they ever did, sat around, doing nothing, just yapping all the time. They had their own club on Thursdays, so why couldn't they stick to that? Or join the Brownies.

After his next go, again brief, he propped his cue and headed for the loo. He recalled the water fights they'd had there and the time they'd hidden all the caps from under the washhand basins, so no one could use them. And the time Simmo had locked himself in, got high on glue and they'd had to break the door down to get him.

He returned to the hall. Baljit was right. He respected her. They'd messed her around something rotten at first, but when she'd made them pay for new fire-extinguishers, they stopped. Also, Baz had called her a

Paki, which was well out of order. He'd been banned for a month for that. Nah, she was alright. And he could talk to her about things. Like girls, or S.S. problems, or doing letters for jobs. She was the only female there not scared of them. But they made things as hard for her as they could. She had some weird ideas. Once, she'd tried to get them all to a film on AIDS, but they didn't want it. Aids depressed him. After all, what was left to them? Their jobs had been taken, so had drugs, and now sex. It wasn't fair. What was there left? Anyway, only homos got AIDS. They were all promiscuous anyway. They deserved all they got. He'd hang them all if he could.

Cliff emerged from his drum session in the lounge, looking thoroughly high on it all. He took a cursory look at a poster advertising the UB40 Club, which was every Friday and usually played some sport or went out in the minibus somewhere. They'd been canoeing, ice-skating, horse riding, even abseiling. Baljit had tried to use it to get them used to writing C.V.s or to taking courses, but they didn't want that. The club was for them, fun, that was all. The one thing in the world that *was* for them.

Cliff came over and joined them. They were starting a new game and, with Jaz, they played pairs.

They all stuck together. They were all from around here and had all been to one or other of the local secondary schools. There was a lot of pressure to be part of the gang. It gave them a power, especially against the club workers. He just went along with it. Again, it was something to believe in. Like the Sky Blues every other Saturday. They all went to the City together and met up in town on Friday nights.

He looked at his watch. It was nearly time to go. He thought about leaving the mess and going early, but it wasn't worth all the hassle next time. It was their club, they had to look after it. He went over to Claire.

'Going soon?'

'Yeh, O.K.' she replied.

'Just finish this, then put it away. Back to mine?'

'Yeh. I fancy some chips.'

'I ain't got enough.'

'I'll pay.'

'No chance.' And he walked back to finish his game of pool.

A TEENAGER'S REPLY

You ask me why the rise in theft,
Why the crime and violence,
Why the loss of humanity,
Why my petty fingers
Nip out a packet of fags,
Why they steal fifty pence
From my mother's purse
Why they snatch the old lady's bag
In the dim-lit subway.
Yet I know no better,
Copying the morality I see about,
Learning as you teach,
Seeing disintegration
And grasping what I can.

Sixty pence for a teaspoon
Which can cost but two to make,
Is theft,
So why not slip it into my pocket?
Fifty pence for a bus fare,
Then the same home again,
Is theft,
So why not scrawl in felt-tip?
Three hundred for a Wembley ticket
Is theft,
So why not smash it up a bit?
Thirty pence for a chocolate bar
Is theft,
So why not slip it in my pocket?
Sixty quid for a TV licence
Is theft,
So why not dodge paying it?
Twenty pounds for a jumper
Is theft,

Twenty-five for jeans
Is theft,
Fifteen for a shirt
Is theft,
Three for a pair of socks
Is theft,
Six for a record
Is theft,
Thirty for a hotel night
Is theft,
Forty-five a week rent
Is theft,
Three hundred a month mortgage
Is theft,
Leaving school with no exams
Is theft,
Y.T.S.
Is theft,
Two-fifty for the pictures
Is theft,
A pound a pint
Is theft,
Sacking a bloke after thirty years
Is theft,
The whole money game
Is theft.

Taking my school milk
Is theft,
Taking my buses
Is theft,
Taking my hospitals
Is theft,
Taking my schools
Is theft,
Taking my council home
Is theft,
Taking my holidays
Is theft,

Taking my parents' pension
Is theft,
Cutting overseas aid
Is theft,
Selling my public assets
Is theft,
Taking my right to choose
Is theft,
Taking my will to live
Is theft,
Taking my freedom
Is theft,
Taking my fun and happiness,
Taking my job and security,
Leaving me with nothing,
Is the greatest theft of all.

So don't you dare complain
About the child who steals,
Taking a mere packet of sweets,
For it is you,
You,
Who have taught me.

Playing in Wood End

SATURDAY NIGHT FEVER

It was Saturday night and Mandy was heading for town. She descended from the No.15 bus in Broad Gate and ran over to shelter under the overhang by Owen Owen's. There was a slow drizzle dulling the evening sky. Claire and Sabrina were there waiting, ready to kill, their make-up adding two years to their seventeen-year-old features. They always said they were twenty-one and never went for a bloke unless he looked at least twenty-three.

They walked briskly down the hill in their smart, tight, thin dresses, arm bracelets and earrings flashing in the reflection of the shop lights. Mandy stopped by one of the windows to pull her dress down a bit and flick her hair back into place, then scampered after the other two as fast as she dare in her high heels.

Groups of lads were already starting to look at them as they entered the Tally Ho. It was a pub which had been converted to give it a trendy night-club atmosphere, with neon lights, plush seats and plenty of plastic. They clacked upstairs, making plans for the night, talking about people at work and always with one eye surveying the beef around.

Some lads wolf-whistled them, but it was far too early to pick anyone up, so they smiled and passed on, making for the bar.

The pub was still filling up when they left, having made it plain to several men who had approached that they were unwelcome, in the most obvious ways possible – usually something in the vein of 'Get lost, you creep', or 'I'd rather sit with Quasimodo.'

From the Tally Ho, they walked up to Nobby's Place, a similar trendy bar, past the short bus queue of cleaners returning home, or people on their way out of town to meet up at a friend's house. It was about ten o'clock and the drizzle had stopped. Groups of young people hung around, some eating chips, others sky-larking, others in couples smooching, heading for the pubs, or just hanging around.

In Nobby's Place, they changed their attitude. They decided to joke around. Standing in the packed bar, they took it in turns to eye fellas up, then ignore them if they approached. Two of them would pick the ugliest or youngest bloke around and the other had to eye him up. Then they picked on one poor lad and all three stared at him without blinking, until he moved away. It was great fun.

After one drink there, they left and walked through the precinct to the Bug And Black Bat. More young people were out now, galavanting around. One man grabbed Sabrina from behind and put her over his shoulders and ran off with her. She screamed, until he put her down then, laughing and bright red, let him kiss her goodbye.

They could hear the sounds of shouting nearby as a fight started. They hurried on, down past the pizza restaurants, with the couples staring into each others' eyes or watching the singing and laughing knots of people go by. Two lads were playing football with an empty coke can, but stopped to wolf-whistle the three young women as they walked past.

They went round by some fountains, where three lads were attempting to push another one in, all singing 'Twenty-one today! Twenty-one today!' and 'Happy Birthday to you.' It was a scatty atmosphere. Crazy, looney, ominous and yet delirious. Young people having fun, letting loose, letting go.

In the Bug, they soon spotted a nice-looking bloke of about thirty and decided to have some fun with him. Mandy was assigned to chat him up. She went over and told him how Claire really fancied him and watched as he went red with embarrassment. He tried his best to be chatty, but all three girls stared at him and wouldn't reply. Sabrina had nudged up beside him, gently squeezing her body against him and then pinched his bum.

Their fun was interrupted when Claire spotted some fellas she knew and they all hurriedly said tarra to the bloke and pushed their way over.

They were her eldest brother's mates and perfect for a good laugh. They all worked and had plenty of money to spend, so decided to go together to Busters night club.

Outside again, the post-war precinct shops seemed boring in their angular, characterless similarity. It was all concrete and glass. A traffic-free pedestrianised shopping centre built from the ashes of the blitz, but left with no old buildings of heritage at all. It was a city centre without residents either. Very few people lived there, making it dead, apart from the pub crawlers.

A police car slowly toured the paved ways, as the three girls and five lads joked their route to the night club. They climbed the stairs and joined the queue waiting to get in. It slowly moved forward, as the bouncers frisked everyone and turned away people incorrectly dressed, or who looked too young.

Once inside, the ear-piercing disco music got the girls swaying their hips and shoulders straight away. They followed the lads to the bar and allowed them to buy the drinks.

After a while, they and the lads set another plan up. They decided to put the crack on a lad. Each of them put two quid into a kitty and bet Sabrina she couldn't get off with him and get him to kiss her on the dance floor. She agreed, and, within ten minutes, was snogging away. Five minutes later, to the lad's chagrin, she had dropped him and come back to claim her winnings.

A man of about twenty-five was eyeing Claire. He leaned nonchalantly against one of the pillars designed to look as though they were carved out of the rock of some cavern. He was flicking a finger in the pocket of his trousers. He was blond, with his hair styled longer at the back and short on top. He had a couple of mates with him equally good looking and Claire smiled back. She suggested a dance to the other two, telling them about the guys and they agreed to go onto the floor and look available.

The three men took their time and the girls had to get rid of several other likely lads before they came over and danced. After a while, they accepted the suggestion of a drink.

Trying to talk over the noise and watching the dance floor, they laughed at a young lad who was barely five-feet tall, but very smooth in his suit, as he tried to move in on one girl after another, but was repulsed each time.

'I couldn't get rid of him one week,' Mandy shouted into Sabrina's ear. 'He had this real corny chat-up line. Said he had his own night club and drove a Masarati. I told him he couldn't reach the pedals, even if he did have one.'

'How'd'you get rid of him?' Sabrina shouted back, still watching the gauche dancing under the strobes and lasers.

'I told him "Go back to mummy, shortie". That upset him. But I didn't care. Little squirt.'

'I'd've said "Shouldn't you be in bed by now"?'

But, beneath this abrasive exterior were warm hearts. It was all image and flippancy. No one wanted to get serious. Everyone wanted fun, to move around, be free'n easy, have a good time. It was for the streetwise, for the best looking and best dressed. It was all impressions and superficiality. That was all they wanted. Yet there was the romance of perhaps picking up a really dishy and affectionate bloke, one who had a sports car and earned ten thousand a year, yet would help with the washing up.

Image, pazzazz, money, flashy clothes, good looks. A good catch, one you could show off. Not personality, not character, nothing serious, first impressions, joking around, laughter. Swept off your feet. Fast chat, fast lay, fast goodbye.

It was the name of the game. They loved the chance to refuse people, but hated being refused. They went for those more attractive and dismissed those who weren't up to their mark. Everyone was the same. There was no point feeling sorry for others, or for yourself. They went out to get who they wanted, every Saturday night.

"I love me, I want the best for me. The best silhouette, the sexiest flickering shape, the juiciest lips, the hunkiest shoulders, the most dominating stranger."

PIGEON PARADE

It's not a bad life, being a pigeon. You get your grub thrown down free, or just waddle around a couple of American tourists sitting on the grass behind the statue of Lady Godiva in Broad Gate, and they even chuck it at you. A life of leisure.

From the top of the National Westminster Bank, you can look down on the buses dropping and picking up their passengers and on the thousands milling about the modern precinct. After a mating dance or two along the parapets, you can glide down past the silver birch trees, past Peeping Tom as he comes out to watch Lady Godiva ride round on her horse as the clock strikes the hour and settle by the queue of customers waiting hours to use a rapid cash till.

You can gobble around a bit, coo at the Japanese (they're suckers for that!), check out for some crusts, then struggle into the air again. You can flap over the walkways, circle over the carparks which curl their way over the roofs of the shops, and float down to the central precinct, where the square is usually full of buskers or a band. There, you can waste a few carefree hours squabbling with tricky-dicky sparrows which nip in and try to whip your dessert.

But, above all, you can sit in the nooks and crannies of the miles of concrete and brick built by some half-blind planner who thought dullness and lack of imagination was preferable to quaintness and tradition, and just doze.

Maria – At the Parson's Nose

MUMMY, I WANT A WEE WEE . . .

Janet had two-year old twins. They were identical little girls and, as everyone kept stopping her to remark, 'Oh, they're *so* sweet. I bet they're little angels, aren't they?'

Little did they know.

A normal, everyday shopping trip into town involved the two darlings, well wrapped up, a double buggy, two bottles of Ribena, a packet of rusks and then, and only then, some plastic bags for the shopping. Boarding a bus was too awful to mention. She had nightmares about it.

Once in town, it was a question of getting round the shops as quickly as possible, hoping they either slept or were at least content enough until she got home.

Janet had just come out of Mothercare, after buying a couple of pairs of toddlers' tights, when Samantha started to cry.

'I want a wee.'

'Wait 'til we get home, Sam,' Janet said calmly.

'I want a wee.'

'Just go to sleep.'

'Mummy, I want a wee wee.'

'Ssshh. We'll be home soon. Here, have a rusk.'

Samantha threw the rusk onto the ground and started to bawl. Janet capitulated.

'Alright, Sam, we'll go to the Ladies.'

She pushed the buggy over to the toilets, which were down a flight of steps, underground. She undid Samantha and then Claire and let them out. The double buggy, heavy with shopping over the back, then fell over, breaking the eggs on the top. She picked the buggy up and took off the bag, then set about getting down the steps. Firstly, she took Sam and the shopping down, then told her to wait whilst she went back up for Claire and the buggy. She collapsed the buggy and walked them down. She then resurrected the buggy, put the shopping in one of the seats and pushed it over to the toilet, the twins trailing, one on each side.

She took Sam into a cubicle, took off her all-in-one romper suit and tights and helped her onto the seat. When she had finished, Janet redressed her, then asked Claire if she wanted to go. Claire shook her head.

'Are you sure, because I'm not coming down here again if you do?'

Claire nodded.

'Are you sure?'

Claire nodded again.

'Come on, do a wee.'

But Claire objected, so Janet left it. She then reversed the process, wheeled the buggy back to the steps, took up Sam and the shopping, then back down again to bring up Claire and the buggy. Then she strapped them in and put the shopping back over one of the handles on the buggy. Just as she started off, Claire said:

'Mummy, I want a wee.'

For a second, she was in serious danger of being throttled.

Janet said she couldn't, and went on pushing the buggy. Claire started to cry.

'Wait 'til we get home Claire.' It was both imploring and threatening.

But the cry got worse and she refused to be bribed with either rusk or Ribena. So it was about turn, back to the steps, unstrap, unload, fold up, descend, ascend, descend, load, push, undress, wait, dress, push, unload, fold up, ascend, descend, ascend, resurrect, strap in, load and push off.

By now, Janet had had enough. Her temper had gone, she was tired and sweaty and completely fed up. She headed for the bus station at Pool Meadow. On the way, the twins drifted off to sleep.

"Why couldn't you have done that an hour ago?" Janet thought. She waited in the bus queue, then had to go through the whole unstrapping, folding and carrying process again, waking up the twins and starting them both off crying again.

The bus journey home was Hell, pure Hell. The twins screamed the whole way.

"Never again," Janet promised herself. "Never again."

But, once through the battle of getting off the bus, the twins fell off to sleep again on the push back to the house. Going along, their eyes closed, with their blond, curly hair and soft, rosy cheeks, they looked divine.

'Oh,' said a lady stranger passing by, 'What angels! I so envy you. I've always wished I'd had twins. You must be so proud of them. But I bet they're little terrors as well, aren't they?'

'Just a little,' Janet said, 'just a little,' as she turned up her pathway and contemplated the bliss of a nice, quiet, relaxing cup of tea.

THE INCONTINENT LAUNDRY SERVICE

In the laundry, the workers were already busy as Glenys started loading the clean sheets into her van. The piles of soiled sheets and the dirty clothes from the residential homes in the city were already being sorted, checked off and put into large boxes for washing. Loads were in from the Chace Hostel, Stoke House and Maurice Edelman House, amongst others. There was also a pile of swimming bath towels, some of which Bill and John, who worked the four large washing machines, had already put in. In a corner, one of the women was putting some trousers into the dry cleaner and Lena was on a pressing machine doing some jackets.

Once washed, the clothes and sheets were shaken out and put through the Callender, a giant mangle which folded them as well. They were then folded some more by a couple of women and passed over to be neatly stacked in the plastic laundry bins they had come in, for the van drivers to take them back.

Although it was only eight in the morning, the heat was already rising. In the height of summer, it was unbearable, even with all the windows open, and they often worked in bikini tops and took their lunch break outside, simply to cool off.

Glenys finished loading. Someone had switched on a radio and it was blaring out over the sound of the foot-presses and washing machines. Her van was partitioned, with the back for the dirty sheets and the part behind the seats for the clean ones.

She strapped herself in, lit a cigarette, turned on the radio and carefully negotiated the parked lorries and cars and turned onto Livingstone Road, heading towards Wyken and her first drop of the day.

There were two of them who did this service, having about two hundred calls a week each. She had spent seven years doing it now. The pay wasn't brilliant, but, after a recent, reluctant strike, they had received a rise. She hated taking industrial action, as had the other city transport drivers who had come out as well, but they had felt it was the only way to show the Council just how desperate their plight had been.

She enjoyed the job. She was her own boss, so long as it was done. She was outside, she met people and she tried to stop and have a little chat with each client and to check they were alright. She had to get on with

65

people, had to be a caring person, otherwise the job wouldn't have suited her. In many ways, she didn't see it as a job in the sense of "just something to earn my keep" at all.

Driving through Foleshill, she headed for Stoke Heath. The first three calls each left their yellow plastic sack in their porch and she merely replaced them with clean sheets. She left enough for a clean pair per night, plus a few draw sheets. Some she called on weekly, others twice a week, depending on their need.

The fourth call was to an old lady. She took the clean sheets with her and went up the path. She entered, announcing herself. The home help was also there, talking with the woman in her front room. Her bed had been brought downstairs for her. She had had a stroke and also broken her arm, which hadn't set properly and was now misshaped into an awkward angle.

She was a very pleasant, unprepossessing woman. She didn't like to bother anyone and often the home help would have to prise her needs out of her. She had only recently come out of hospital, part of the exercise to cut the waiting lists, but Glenys felt she should still be there. She could do very little for herself and would sit all day in the armchair in her front room, perhaps read the paper and eat the meals left for her by the home help. She also had a flask made up for her. Her relatives all had cars, but never came to see her.

After chatting a while, Glenys returned to her van, throwing the sack of dirty sheets into the back. Carrying those sacks was a heavy task.

Then onto the next, a man who looked after his wife. She handed over the clean sheets and picked up the old.

On the dashboard was her daysheet, with the list of her calls, the type of sheets to be left and how many.

Quite often, one of her elderly people would die. She saw a lot of death, sometimes two or three a week. If Social Services knew about it, before she was due to deliver, they would tell her. Otherwise, she and Doris would scan the "Evening Telegraph" and, if one had died, they would leave it for a week before calling to collect the sheets. They had to use their own judgement about how affected the bereaved would be.

Some elderly gradually worsened and she would be watching them slowly fade away. Others, it would come as a surprise. One man of ninety-six, who had been very frail, but had a very sharp mind and knew everything about Coventry, had been very chirpy one week. She had later found out that he had died just half an hour later.

It was acutely embarrassing at times. Once, she had walked into a house to find the coffin being taken out and a hearse waiting in the street. She'd felt awful.

She had also seen how people cope with death. Some of the bereaved tried not to show anything. They may have lived with the person suffering for many years and see the death as a blessing for both of them. They may have had years to come to terms with death and become hard and blasé about it. But many were so terribly upset that they would cling to her, talk, or just want her to be around. They would cope very badly with it and become disorientated, especially if their whole lives had been intertwined with their partner. They would still cook for two at times, or make two cups of tea. They would still call to the other person, or talk to them, or reach for them in bed. It created a huge gap in their lives and often, because they were both propping each other up, once one died, the bereaved rapidly lost the will to live and would follow within a year.

She drove down Henly Road into Walsgrave, where she dropped off some sheets for a woman who was severely handicapped. She was only thirty-three. She had some wonderful chidren, who helped her to cope. It was a remarkable family, very resilient in the face of such heartache, especially as the eldest child was in and out of hospital and was bed-wetting as well.

The next was just a drop-in. A quick knock, a hello, an exchange of sheets.

She saw a lot of suffering and a lot of caring as well. There had been a man suffering from multiple sclerosis, who had left his wife to live with his parents. His father had then died leaving his mother to look after him and, although she herself had had cancer, she had ignored her own illness to concentrate on getting treatment for her son. She had eventually died and he was now in a home.

Some neighbours were very caring, but often a family would try to hide its problems from them. Some people were too embarrassed to leave the sheets in the porch, whilst others refused to admit they were incontinent, until they couldn't cope any more. Usually, when neighbours did know, they would call in and keep an eye on the elderly person.

The next call was to a family where the wife had died. The father now looked after his two teenage sons, who were both mentally handicapped, and his twin daughter who had muscular distrophy and was still at home. That too, was a very caring family.

Next, a young man in his dressing gown brought out the sheets used by his young wife. Then off to another, where an elderly lady pottered to the door. She and her husband lived in a sheltered flat unit.

This job gave her glimpses of an unknown world, hidden behind closed doors, tucked away out of sight. There was such a contrast between how people lived. One street could be so nice, the next one clearly in poverty. It was pitiful to see the other end of life, the damp and the disrepair some houses descended into.

She drove to the next client, heading back towards Henly. At this one she had to be careful. The man was incontinent, but his wife would often not leave the old sheets out. Sure enough, there were only the draw sheets left. Glenys asked her about the others. She denied having had them, but Glenys didn't believe her. She had to be firm, because she suspected the woman might be selling the sheets off to her relatives.

Then into Wood End, firstly to a very elderly woman who was being looked after by her son, then to the district Social Services office, to pick the sheets up from a household where the man had a history of violence.

She headed back to the Livingstone Road laundry with her full load. Mornings were always more of a rush than the afternoons, because she needed to call on a lot of the clients before they went off to the Day Centres, and if she was late or missed them, some of the elderly could get quite upset. They looked forward to her visits, they knew the time she knocked and so would go to the door. She may be the only person they saw all day. She was very important to some of them. That was why she always went with a cheerful smile, despite what she might feel inside. There was no place for sulking in her job.

She arrived back, reversed the van towards the unloading bay and hauled out the stinking sheets, throwing the sacks onto a large mound already waiting to be washed. She then lit another cigarette and drove back out, to Bell Green this time.

One call was to a lady looking after her wheelchair-bound husband. She was a frail little thing, whilst he was about sixteen stone, yet she had to lift him in and out of bed and into the wheelchair. Then on to a lady who was slightly senile, then into Wood End again, to call on a woman looking after her mother, a man whose wife was incontinent. Some of the elderly had no washing machine. For them, such an item was still a luxury. This couple were obviously deeply in need as well. There were no carpets on the floor and the walls were bare, except for a thin wash of paint.

The next stop was back in Bell Green, to call on a woman in a ground-floor flat. She shouted out and went in. The woman was in her wheelchair and her home help was doing her hair. She worked closely with the other elderly services, the health visitors and home helps, to keep an eye on their clients, especially those whose family never called. For them, their relations would only come when they had died. Once, the family of an old woman was busy fighting over the laundry service's sheets, whilst she was still dying. They were vultures, people like that.

Glenys had lived in Coventry for most of her life and had a daughter. Her father had come to the city to work (delivering cars), for Jaguar, then moved on to Betterware, Morris engines, and city engineers as an electrician. A lot of people had come into the city in the boom years, but with the unemployment, a lot were now moving out again, especially the retired and the young. She herself was petrified of going back onto social security. She could never manage on it. She had seen people who had tried, who had attempted to remain cheerful, clean and tidy, but who had ended up on anti-depressants.

She felt the community spirit had gone from the city. There was some coming back for City reaching the cup final, but compared to other cities and countries, there was little pride in the place, little identity with it, or feeling that it was "our" city. The factories had gone, there was less control over the young, more violence and hostility. She didn't find Coventry a friendly city at all. No one would speak to her here. There was a fear. She daren't look anyone in the eyes, less they take offence. The city centre was full of trouble at night. The gangs were far worse now, with knives and hatchets and even sawn-off shotguns. But what did the youth have? The dole at sixteen? There were leisure facilities, but who wanted to go weight-lifting every day?

Driving down towards Gosford Green, she turned into one of the streets by Kingsway, drawing up alongside an elderly man who was leaning awkwardly against the post which had once held his garden gate. It was only a tiny front garden. He greeted Glenys as she got out of the van. He only had one leg and put his weight back onto his two walking sticks as she squeezed past him and entered the hall. There was no carpet on the floor, which was very dusty. The front room was never used and the front door had been smashed in by some yobs a while ago and had not been repaired. He lived in his back room, where he had a chair, a T.V., a small piece of carpet and the settee on which he slept. His clothes were old, fraying and were starting to smell. He obviously needed a lot of care, but there was no one to help him. One more of the forgotten ones.

She drove back to the laundry for her ten-twenty tea break, unloaded the van again, then parked it by the yard stacked high with coal for the laundry boilers and for the swimming baths next door. She went in a side entrance, through the laundry room and up the stairs to the dining area. It wasn't a proper canteen, as no meals were laid on, but they had a cooker and a kettle, so they could brew up when necessary. That was one of Lena's jobs. She was the chargehand in the laundry and was soon shouting 'Tea Up!' over the noise of the radio.

Glenys slumped into a chair and had another cigarette. Lena offered to make her some toast. There were several tables and chairs around, covered in coats, cardigans and bags of shopping. It was a relaxed, trusting atmosphere. As the women came in, they paid Lena what they owed her for their batches and cakes, as it was also her task to visit the local bakery every morning.

Glenys chatted away the tea break, then rose with the others to return to work. She drove the van round to the loading bay, then pushed another trolley of clean sheets over to it and loaded up again.

She called on an old lady who was stone deaf and who relied on her dog to tell her someone was there, then to Stoke Green, to a very posh semi, with nicely kept garden and a garage, before driving to the office in the city centre, where all the Council transport services were co-ordinated. There was Dial-A-Ride, a taxi service for the handicapped, Mobile Meals, which provided over nine hundred meals a day to twelve hundred people a week and ambulances which took the elderly to six different day centres and to various luncheon clubs. These together provided a subtle link between all the services for the elderly in the city.

The largest service was for the mentally handicapped. Three hundred adults were taken to five different centres and workshops each day and a hundred children to three special schools. Trips were organised for people in residential homes and for charity organisations which had no transport of their own. There was, in fact, a holidays and entertainments section, which used hotels on the coast which specialised in the disabled.

Seventy-five per cent of the staff were woman, many of whom were part-time. They had a basic training and had to have an accident-free licence, but the main qualification was their attitude of mind. They had to be caring people.

Her final two calls of the morning were typical. The first was to an old man. He had, as usual, left his sheets in the front room. It was a tip, a junk yard, stinking and full of flies. The place had not been decorated in decades and the poor man, living in his kitchen, feared putting on the fires because of the bills. He was typical of some elderly who wanted to stay out of a home, in their own house, who needed a lot of support, yet weren't getting it, because of the intense pressure on the social services.

Her last call was to an old couple in a large private house which again had fallen into decay. Most of the elderly couldn't do repairs and usually those in private houses were worse off than those in Council property, where the Council maintained them. She went through the garden to the back door. The kitchen, where they left the old sheets, had damp walls and some of the plaster was cracking as well. She popped her head into the dining room to say hello, have a quick chat, and make sure they were alright, then went back to her van.

She sighed, lit up another cigarette and headed back to the laundry.

Shopping in Foleshill

71

NURSERY NURSE

In my mind I can see you,
Bending over that same old jigsaw,
Two of its three pieces missing,
Changing a disgusting nappy,
Ordering one child to refrain
From beating the Hell out of another,
Merinka to cease disembowelling teddy,
Or Elena to stop trying to pull
The head off the gerbil.

It's a tough job,
Parenting a room of toddlers,
Trying to care and educate
And to cling to some remnants of sanity
In a world where so many tiny people
Are totally dependent on you,
Each demanding your love as if
She were the only one in your heart.
Task after inexorable task,
Catastrophe following catastrophe,
As the kids do things you thought
Were impossible,
Or reach parts you thought
Kids couldn't reach,
Being spewed upon,
Sensing warm wetness emanating from
Little bottoms into your overalls,
Thinking – Oh what a mistake! –
You'd let the little ones try painting,
Just for a change,
Then spending an hour
Getting Gemma's hair from blue to normal,
Or mopping Emilie's shoe-prints from the floor.

As calm inches back,
You watch Nathan practice
His Incredible Hulk impersonation
On a terrified little Alexander,
Whilst pinning their latest offerings
On the walls,
Optimistically labelling
Indecipherable blotches and squiggles
As:
'My mum going shopping, with the dog, and a fire
engine';
Watching hopefully for the rain to stop,
So you can get them outside,
Gain a little space
And let them scream off their pent-up energy;
Trying to get Jason to finish his breakfast
Before tea-time,
Praying that at least a couple would sleep,
Then put off your dinner
By a runny nose
Getting runnier and runnier,
And trying to get the brats
To eat their carrots
– Which you secretly hate yourself –
Nearly throttling one of them
For spitting a mouthful onto the floor.

A marvellous occupation,
The wonder of all parents,
And object of their condolences,
Admiring your dedication
And secretly thanking the heavens
There are still people daft enough
To be nursery nurses.

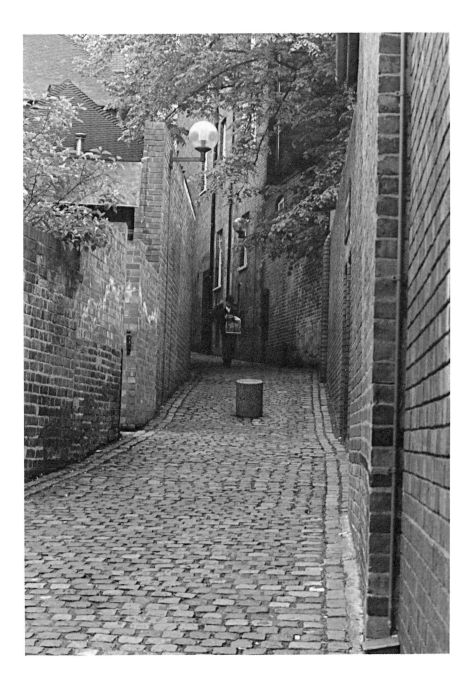

Hill Top

THE WOMEN'S SHELTER

It was a terrible thing to have to do. Awful. Just awful.

The humiliation Jaswinder felt as she knocked on the door of the Cyrenians was excrutiating. It was against everything she had ever been told, it was placing herself on the charity of others, admitting she was a failure. But what choice had she?

Holding her two plastic bags tightly, she knocked again. A young white woman came to the door and invited her in.

'I'm most sorry. I'm so sorry about this.'

'Come into the office. It's warmer in there.'

'I think I should go. You can't help me.'

'It's alright. We're here to help. Please, come in.'

'No, I'd better go.'

'At least tell me why you came. There must have been a reason.'

The twenty-seven year old Sikh woman stared at the ground and broke into silent tears, trying to hide her eyes with her chunnie.

'Come on in,' April said, in a dulcet, welcoming accent. 'I'll make you some hot tea.'

Jaswinder followed her. She was taken into the warmth of the cosy front room.

The short-stay house where Jaswinder was taken had four bedrooms, which she shared with two other women in similar situations. There was also a communal T.V. lounge and a kitchen. They didn't have a rota for cooking because Julie liked it, whereas Brenda preferred to wash and tidy up. Jaswinder, unused to English food, usually cooked separately.

There was a nice atmosphere in the house. It was very supportive. No one pried, but they listened to each other's problems and, one thing she'd started to really enjoy, they could talk and talk until late at night.

One evening, after they had all sat watching Dallas, they started to chat. Brenda had had a very rough time with her husband. She was in her mid-thirties and had suffered beatings for years. She had only stayed because of her two children, but had finally been unable to take any more. It was the marital problems of J.R. and Sue-Ellen which sparked her off.

'She ought to leave him.'

'She never will. She's got it made there. I wouldn't leave if I was her.'

'The money ain't worth it.'

75

'It is, if you've got as much as she has.'

'Look. Look. My old man, you know, he was rolling in it, but all he ever did was drink.'

'Not all men are like that.'

'I bet your old man hit you.'

'Yea, but . . . '

'Yea, they're all the same. I hate all men.'

'Don't be stupid.'

'You ain't been through what I have.'

Jaswinder, listening and gaining courage to join in, spoke.

'My husband used to hit me all the time. I had to accept it. I think every man hits women. It's natural.'

'Did you have one of them arranged marriages?'

'Yes. He lived up in Newcastle. After we were married, I wanted to move up there with him, but he said he had to get the house ready, so I went to live with his parents in Leicester. His parents kept asking him why he wasn't letting me go to Newcastle. He said it was because of the house. When I went up there, I found he already had a wife and two children.'

'What, married to her an' all?'

'Yes. She was an English woman. He was very apologetic. He got me another house so I could live there, but he wanted to have me and this other woman. I wouldn't have it, so he hit me. I went back to my parents three or four times, but they always sent me back.'

'Why did they do that? Surely they could see your bruises?'

'They said I had to accept it. I'd made my bed, so I had to sleep in it. His parents felt terrible about it when they found out. They wanted me to marry their other son.'

'I don't know what I'd have done without my mum and dad,' Julie interrupted. 'They put me up when I left before. But I went back.'

'We all do,' Brenda said. 'We must all be insane. I went back six times. He broke my arm once and still I went back.'

'We've got nowhere to go.'

'John knew I'd be there, so he'd come round after a few days with some flowers and a box of chocolates and tell me how much the kids were missing me and I'd give in. This time, I came here, so he'll never find me. I'll get a bedsit or flat. I might move to Birmingham. I've got friends there.'

'The trouble with my husband,' Jaswinder said, 'was his drinking. He got so bad when he drank.'

'So many men drink a lot.'

'You're telling me. The drink was always out. He was very well educated, you know. He wanted his children to be doctors. Even his girl he wanted to go to college.'

'I thought they didn't care about girls' education.'

'A lot's changed. If it means a better marriage, we do. You see, it's all about prestige with us. A big car, a big house, a doctor for a son, an educated daughter, a lot of drink out for our guests. That way we can tell our friends and relations how successful we are. The family's much more important for us than for you. If we're bad, it makes the whole family bad. That's why they sent me back all the time. That's why I hated to come here and I don't want them to know I'm here. Last time I went to the Panh-ghar, a sheltered home for Asian women, but my father found it. I'd die if he found me here.'

'You wouldn't. You'd be alright.'

'I've thought about suicide.'

'So've I.'

'And me. Loads of times. Too many times.'

'You'll soon find a place of your own.'

'I hope so.'

'Are you looking for a job yet?'

'Not really. I haven't even thought about that at all. I want a place of my own first. Or I'll run away. I don't know what to do.' The strain was obviously affecting her and she started to cry.

'I hated coming here as well,' said Julie. 'I thought the Cyrenians were all about men in night shelters. I thought there was nowhere. I didn't want to go to a battered wives' home. I don't know. I never felt it was that bad. I wasn't really battered. I just had to get out. He used to lock me up in that house. I could never go out without him. He never gave me any money. He made sure I knew who was the boss. I couldn't take it any more.'

'We used to row like blazes.'

'So did we.'

'We never,' said Jaswinder. 'I never had the courage. We don't. He was my husband, which meant I should never argue. I had to be obedient all the time. When I told my mother-in-law, she got so angry with me and told me I should be grateful to have a roof over my head. They didn't understand anything that was going on. She came over from the Punjab. She didn't accept western ways. To her, marriage was for ever and that was that. She was as bad, in her way. She never let me go out on my own. She said it wasn't right, people would talk and say "Look at her, she lets her daughter-in-law walk the streets all hours of the day". I had to obey her in the house. She told me what to cook and what to buy and what housework to do. Then we had to serve the men and, after the meal, we had to retire to let the men talk on their own. But I still had to stay up until the guests left and all the men went to bed. It wasn't done for me to go to bed before them, no matter how late it might be. I was there in case they needed anything and that was it.'

'I wouldn't have put up with that.'

'It's a different culture, though, isn't it. They're taught differently. Our ways must be strange to them.'

'I felt terrible about leaving the kids,' Julie said, rising out of the chair. 'Terrible. Anyone want coffee?'

'I'd murder one.'

'Yes, please.'

'You see, I'm thirty-eight now and we've got two boys. Robert's thirteen and Neil's eleven. They need their dad more than me. They used to side with him. Neither of them were mummy's boys. I wish they had been. I wish I'd had a daughter, someone to talk to. That's what some women do, you know, they try to turn their son into a daughter, make him soft and dependent on her. It's so she's not on her own against her old man. It's all about sides. The battle lines go right down the middle, I can tell you.'

Whilst Brenda was saying this, Julie had gone into the kitchen to make the coffees. The news was on the T.V. and there was some report about this being the Year of the Homeless. Tens of thousands of people were homeless, it said. Either sleeping rough on the streets, or in hostels, or sharing a floor with a friend or relation. A growing number were women.

'You know April, the worker who comes here? She said the Cyrenians had forty-four women come in to them in the last two months in Coventry.'

'That's nearly one a day.'

'Yea. There's a lot of young ones, she says, kicked out by their parents.'

'I can never understand that. We would never do that.'

'I think families are breaking down. No one believes in the family any more. If the kids can't get jobs, their parents aren't going to support them. The pressure's too much. It isn't worth it.'

'We grew up in a shop.'

'Oh yea, where?'

'It was a grocery shop on the Stoney Stanton Road. We always run grocery shops, don't we,' Jaswinder smiled. 'I was born in it. We had five in our family. A lot of our parents set up shops when they came over here. A lot of Sikhs were used to running farms or small businesses in India, whereas so many English people only know about working in a factory for other people. But now quite a lot of us work in sweat shops. I was lucky. I wanted to be a nursery nurse, but my father said, not unless I accepted the arranged marriage. When I agreed to marry Ranjeev, he let me go on a course in nursery nursing first. So I've got some training behind me. The first job I got after I went up to Newcastle was in a private nursery. That factory was a sweat shop. It was run by an Indian and he only employed Indian women. Only a few spoke English. There was no union or anything. But the owner of the house where we had the nursery tried to put up the rent. He said that it would be thirty pounds a week and promised to give us a contract. But, after two weeks, we still didn't have one and he put the rent up to seventy-five pounds a week. We couldn't afford that. Those private nurseries are all about money and not the development of the children. They don't think, "Is that child happy?"'

'So, where were you before you arrived here?'

'I left again about a month ago and came back to my parents in Coventry. They told me to go back again. I wanted to kill myself. Then I decided to come here.'

'When did your parents come over here?'

'Dad came in fifty-four and mum in fifty-seven. They bought their first shop in fifty-nine.'

'Where did they come from?'

'The Punjab.'

'Where's that?'

'In north India, by Pakistan. They'd all heard of Blackpool. Everyone from India wants to visit Blackpool. When they came over here, there was only one Sikh in Coventry who could speak English and drive a car. He used to do all the weddings. He's a little old man. He still sells Indian sweets in a little shop in Red Lane.'

Julie came back in with the coffees and the sugar bowl.

'I wish you wouldn't let Tom come round so often, Julie,' Brenda said. 'I want to get away from men.'

'He's my brother. He's alright.'

'No man's alright. Any man could rape a woman.'

'He doesn't come very often.'

'Men should be banned from this house. They shouldn't be allowed in, ever.'

'Well, Tom's been a real friend to me.'

'Meet him outside then.'

'I do a lot of times.'

'God,' Brenda added, 'men've got it all their own way. Even when they're homeless, they've got a lot more hostels and houses for them. You know, I bet those forty-four women were just the tip of the iceberg. I bet there are hundreds every month who leave, but stay with relatives.'

'Men can get away with a lot more than we can. It's more acceptable. You know, like we have to wear mascara and nail polish, whereas they can come in all oily and smelly. It's alright for them. You see a bloke rolling a cigarette and it's fine, real macho, but a woman, oh no.'

'I'd never roll a cigarette.'

'I don't smoke,' Jaswinder said.

'But I think we're stronger. Men are so pathetic at times. At least we know what we want. We have a lot more about us, a lot more responsibilities than men. We're used to coping with crises. We don't let ourselves go like some of the men do. I think we're much stronger.'

'Men can get away with murder. They can go into pubs on their own, get drunk, knock off as many women as they like, and it's all a big joke. But if we did that, we'd be called slags.'

'What's a slag?' Jaswinder asked.

'Don't ask.'

'One of them fallen women. Or that's what men like to think,' Julie enlightened her. 'Where we fall down is, we put up with too much. We're all scared of leaving them. They've got all the money. We can't get jobs. We'd end up on the streets.'

'What I used to do,' Brenda interrupted, 'was go from one rotten situation to another. You know. I married John to get out of my parents', then when I left him, I kept going back there. But that was no good. They let me stay, but it was awful for them, John coming round and us having screaming rows outside their house. That's why I went back. I'd nowhere else to stay, when it came down to it.'

'I felt so guilty about leaving an' all.'

'Oh, I know, it's terrible.'

'I felt it was all my fault. I felt I *had* to make it work.'

'Well, every woman I've ever talked to's said her old man hits her. But they don't leave. They stick it.'

'They shouldn't though, should they.'

'They've got no choice.'

'I like this house,' Jaswinder said, suddenly changing the subject. 'It's warm and I feel safe.'

'It's not what I thought the Cyrenians would be,' Brenda added. 'It's been a real life-saver. Except for the occasional man, that is.' She looked at Julie.

'Men aren't really allowed in, Brenda. Tom's been twice in two weeks, that's all. Some women wouldn't come if it was no men at all. You've got to give and take a little.'

'Well,' said Jaswinder, 'all I know is, it's saved me from the streets. I don't know what I'd've done otherwise. Probably killed myself. At least I don't feel like that any more.'

THE BINGO PLAYER

May shows her Granada card,
Pays her entrance fee,
Takes her summer specials
And walks through glittering doors
Into a theatre of light and sound,
Of T.V.s, bars and buffets,
Of laughter, drinks and chat,
And scuttles over to Rita and Joan,
Sitting in their usual place.

As she walks between the tables,
She remembers her work tomorrow,
Another day of assembling parts,
Forseeing every wire she will solder
And component she will piece together.
Leisure and between-work hours
Are, for her
Merely time away from work.

She works shifts,
Time and motion any hour a day,
A week on nights,
Then days, then mornings,
Not knowing when to cook,
Dreading the alarm
And learning to sleep alone,
Though she would still roll over
And her outstretched arm
Seach vainly for her husband's warmth.

She decides to visit the buffet
For Maltesers and crisps,
Then seeks out the bar
For half a lager and lime,
Before the caller comes on,
Asking them to return
And open to their pages of pink,
Their first number for a line.

She rushes back,
Pen out,
Listening hard
In the perfect silence
Of people concentrating to win.
The line called,
Her mind drifts to her family,
Three teenage lads,
Making work and home
A double-shift life,
Where leisure barely exists,
But is a constant rush
To do the chores
Before work begins again,
And where the production line
Means she is no longer "Ma!",
But one of the girls,
Herself in herself.

Once more the standing jester
Calls out numbers over the tannoy
To the hushed punters,
As eighty-eight flashes up,
After sixty-six,
On the glaring T.V. sets
And Rita wins her first line for months,
Then smiles at her friends and discusses
Buying a secret bottle
To make the insistence of work
Pass a little less painfully:
A little rebellion
Against the regime imposed from birth
Upon a race dictated to by timetables,
Forced to conform,
Set times at work imposing
Set times at home,
The never-ending metronome
Of domestic tasks
Beating their own time.

Then to the next page,
And the line again,
Until another shout shatters

The tensely attentive air
And a young woman counts out
The winning numbers
On the woman's card
And four hundred pages of grey are ripped
And four hundred of mauve begun,
With felt-tips hovering,
Dashing up and down
Five or six frantic books at a time,
Until another full-house call
And the silence breaks to a buzz
Then crescendoes
Into the relaxed laughter
Of between-sessions talk.

Her husband passes, some weeks,
On the doorstep,
And her children are strangers
In her clock-geared life
Of piece-rate and bonus.
The metabolic stress keys her up,
As she misses the Friday nights
And weekends in bed
Most would take for granted,
Envying those on regular hours,
Who live conjointly with the world,
Wondering,
If there is no life in life,
If there is life after life,
The repetition of the seconds
Reflecting
The repetition of the line.

The American Game is called,
As quiet falls again.

"Blue, three-oh, thirty;
White, four and one, forty-one;
Red, on its own, number nine . . . "

A woman in green collects glasses
Before the National Game,
Worth forty thousand,

Then the mid-evening special,
The T.V.s beaming the numbers called,
The winning number flashing,
Then switching back
To silent images of Brookside.
The three saunter off
To stretch their legs,
Leaving coats and books
To reserve their seats,
Visiting the loo or shop,
Risking the fruit machines,
Stopping off at the prize bingo
Still rattling away in a corner,
Slipping ten pees into a slot
And flicking plastic covers
Over the numbers
As they are called,
Until the buzzer goes again
And they scurry back
To settle to a hush.

Time is money,
Every facet of the plant
Is down to time,
To speeding up,
More parts in less minutes,
A D-minus life,
Where even leisure has to be rushed
To get enough in,
Carbondating her mind,
Through decade, year and season,
To day and minute,
And an infinity of seconds.

Boredom?
What was boredom?
The luxury of nothing to do,
Of quietly staring through rainy windows,
Of kicking sand on the shore,
Was unknown to her,
Except in an occasional holiday by the sea,
A brief time without time,
When time and tide wait for everyman,

The ticking of the clocks is drowned
In the midst of carefreeness
And the alarm sings a gentle song,
Lulling the sleeper to softer slumber,
When time dissolves
And free from it at last,
She could attain her human stature
And not be a slave.

A voice cries "Time, ladies, please!"

As they rise to leave,
Collecting umbrellas and scarves,
To take a taxi home,
As time elapses and future merges
Into present, then past,
Her youth into her old age,
She becomes aware of her transcience,
Her unimportance,
Of life gone and to come,
Yet of endurance:
As mortal,
Condemned to death
As soon as born,
And immortal,
Since she lives
The duration of the universe,
Beginning at her birth,
Ending at her death:
A fleeting span which, for her,
Is forever.

MR BIG

Sitting in a crowded Mr Big at about half five in the evening, I see a man entering the café being stopped by the floor manageress.

He is middle-aged, bedraggled, in a worn, but not unrespectable coat, a large scab on his right cheekbone and untidy, though not unkempt, hair. He is obviously homeless, wanting to while away some time over a cup of tea. But the woman tells him politely he has to go. Quietly, without any fuss, he asks again, then, refused, turns and hobbles off.

The manageress turns to her staff and says:

'That's my third today.'

She raises three of her fingers, laughing as if in triumph.

'That's my third,' she says. 'That's my third.'

HAWKING

As I walked along the Moorfield, in the old part of Stoke Aldermoor, I noticed a man, twenty-eight or so, working his way up and down each path with a supermarket basket on his arm, full of packets of sweets. It was a beautiful day and the pre-war houses, whilst not sparkling, seemed a lot less grey.

The residents, mainly elderly who had lived on the estate since it had been built and new, young couples gradually replacing them, bought a few from the hawker, but most didn't.

Walking on, I glanced down The Barley Lea towards the new estate of the Pondfield and the Boxhill, built in the fifties of the same disastrous no-fines concrete as Wood End, with its poor insulation and unstable foundations. The Pondfield was being converted into modern flats by a private developer, to get it off Council hands. Down there, where unemployment was grim and the kids had little to look forward to, another man, about twenty, was having more success with his sweets.

HAND-OUT

As I passed a church hall, I noticed a long queue of people outside, waiting for their free hand-out of EEC butter, cheese and UHT milk. Coventry had been allocated two tons of butter and the only way the powers that be could think of distributing it was in a way guaranteed to be the most humiliating and patronising.

Many really in need would never dare join the begging queue for neighbours to see. Those who had, grasped their allowance books and pension books, waited hours in the cold rain, then had their books branded with the letters "M + B" as evidence of their visit.

The volunteers handing it all out felt humiliated as well and let down by the bad organisation, which meant that many who queued still got nothing. The hopes of pensioners raised then dashed.

Perhaps the greatest tragedy was not that they missed the butter that once, but that they miss it every day simply because it is just too expensive. Like all sudden charity, it did more to expose the extent of the problem than it ever did to solve it.

SAINSBURY'S

Walking past Sainsburys' in the January snow, I hear the noise of a fight just behind me. The first reaction is to get out of the way as fast as I can, but then I turn to see what's happening.

It's from just inside the supermarket's doors. One man is trying to get out, whilst another tries to push him in. Others, in the chocolate brown of the Sainsburys' staff, come to try to restrain the man and I know immediately what it's all about.

What shocks me most is the silence of it all. The man doesn't scream, he merely pushes and struggles. His eyes meet mine as he is slowly hauled back inside and as he knows he has been caught. Doubtless, that petrified, silent stare hid dramas of police and court and prison cell.

The new year. The season of goodwill.

THE FORGOTTEN ONES

The forgotten ones,
Crouching behind locked doors,
Limping to fill kettles under dripping taps,
Left alone in wheelchairs,
Unable to dress or wash or shave,
Watching their houses decay about them,
Ignored by relatives,
Ignorant of help,
Too proud to admit they cannot cope,
Scraping existence in dirt and cold,
Without curtains or carpets,
Without hot water or heat,
Without washing machine or radio,
Without chairs or cookers,
Without life,
As life passes by,
In the glint of light
From an open letterbox.

JACKO

Jacko was in a bit of a fix. You see, he'd been alright that morning until then. He'd had a few shakes when he'd got up in the cold of his bedroom, but a quick shot had calmed him and he'd been alright since then. Quite confident in fact. And that had been the trouble.

You see, unlike everyone else, who had just sat down at the tables and waited to be served, he had decided to demand a tray and carry his Christmas dinner over by himself.

"Why was I so stupid?" he thought, as panic rapidly gripped him and the shakes took sudden, violent control of his whole body. He just managed to lower the vibrating plates onto the long table which ran along the wall and was decorated with piles of mince pies, slices of Christmas pudding, Christmas cakes, and much else.

There was a Christmas cracker on the table by his tray. He hadn't touched one since he'd been a kid. He reached out his hand and caressed it, stroking the red crepe, gently squeezing the stiff tube of card and delicately feeling the gold sticker which read "Merry Xmas" with his fingertips. So long. It had been so long.

He looked around, too humiliated to ask for help, or to accept it when a young woman helper offered to take his tray. Oh, why was he so pig-headed? Why was he so stupid? Wasn't there a hole he could crawl down? Couldn't he disappear under the table?

He wished he hadn't come. Trying again to lift the tray, it was worse now. The tension and confusion of his mind paralysed his legs, whilst sending his arms into uncontrollable spasms. Oh, he wanted to cry.

The rest of the diners, mostly men, of all ages, but with the common fate of being homeless or on their own for Christmas, were sitting down, busy stuffing themselves with the turkey. Volunteers were rushing about serving them, opening cans of Barbican, pouring orange squash, or, best of all, giving each a half-ounce packet of Old Holborn and a packet of Rizlas. Jacko desperately watched as everyone but him was getting one.

He tried to lift his tray again, but managed only a few seconds before the irrepressible shaking started again. His feet seemed sunk in concrete, whilst his legs had lost all bone. It took an enormous effort to move. He just wished he could become one of the flowers on the wallpaper. He was desperate for a drink. The panic suddenly gushed over him again, in a new wave. Nothing to drink! Oh, horror! He could survive without a bottle, so long as he knew he could get one, but when he couldn't, the very thought of the pain, the headaches and stomach cramps made him sweat profusely and cry in despair. All he needed was a little sip of alcohol on his lips, that was all. Just the reassuring flavour and knowledge that his friend was there to comfort him if he was needed.

He wiped a dribble from his chin with the sleeve of his thin, burgundy velvet jacket. He had bought it at the Nearly New Shop for thirty pence. He didn't have an overcoat. Only a long scarf, a pair of brown corduroy trousers and trainers on his feet.

He lived alone in a house which was damp and cold, with only one old gas fire in the sitting room. He had a meter and was sure the landlord had fixed it. Whatever, he couldn't afford to heat the room. The curtains and carpet were bare, the window frames totally rotten, rattling in the slightest breeze. He'd complained about the wallpaper peeling off and the large patches of black mould on the walls, but what did the landlord care? He didn't want to be thrown onto the street. Who'd take a drunk, a hopeless drunk like him? So he sat in his filthy armchair, heated a can of soup on his old gas stove, went into town to walk around, or stopped in the warmth of the library.

It was an old terraced house in Foleshill, down a small side street. A small front garden, barely a yard between the door and the gap where a gate had, long ago, once been. The glass in the door was missing and a board had been nailed up instead. Inside, a dark, dank passage, without lighting. Then an ill-fitting door into the sitting room, where his one chair cowered close to the fire, without the company of any other furniture, not even a table. Then a tiny kitchen, so bitterly cold, old cans littering the floor around the bin, some dozen or so empty bottles on the table and very little food in stock perhaps a few slices of bread, a scrape of jam. No more. This, in fact, was to be his first decent meal for many months. A derelict house and a derelict body. He felt so ashamed and so humbled by the kindness of the helpers around him.

He looked at his plate and picked up a piece of turkey and ate it. it was delicious, melting in his mouth, but was already getting cold. "Oh, help me, someone, please. Carry me over and feed me. Please. Someone."

But when someone did ask, he insisted he was alright. Behind him, in the large kitchen of the Trinity Church Hall, at least a dozen volunteers were dishing out heavily laden plates of Christmas dinner. Others were washing up. Some were carrying the meals out to the diners and collecting the finished plates. Some were serving the Christmas pudding already, laced with cream, and bowls of fruit salad.

Jacko looked plaintively as he was missing out. He stared at the long tables covered with holly, crackers, cans of beer, cups and plates of food being hungrily devoured by the hardy homeless. It was a fine spread and Jacko felt the sharpness of guilt as he remembered the many families who would be having far less than this, who struggled continuously to make ends meet by themselves.

He knew what! Do a roll up. Have a smoke, that'd calm him down fine. He reached into his pocket and pulled out his baccy tin. Opening the lid, he slipped out a Rizla and delicately laid a thin brown line of shag onto it, then, between thumbs and forefingers, expertly juggled and rolled the paper into a cigarette, sealing it with a lick. He lit up, still standing there by the table, his tray of dinner beside him and dragged away his fear.

With the roll-up in his mouth, he felt calm enough to risk the journey to the nearest empty seat. It was as if the presence of something in his mouth had restored his total being and given back his confidence. The five yard trip was slow, but incident-free. He sat down and, relieved, picked up his knife and fork to eat. He was only twenty-three.

ONE MAN—NINE LIVES

He wandered into Norton House, having dawdled down from his one-bedroomed flat in Hillfields. It was a short walk, down the hill and past the small Swanswell Lake and the new, modern bus garage, built in brick. He had noticed how the buses were better housed and looked after than he was.

There were already about ten men sitting or standing around in the bare hall. He greeted most of them, whom he knew well. Then, following his daily routine, he went through to the office to say hello to the staff and hear what was passing. It was locked and there was no answer, so he sauntered back along the hall and looked at the noticeboard, between watching his two fingers roll a cigarette. There was nothing new. A trip to Wales in the offing, and the usual notices about no drinking or drugs and one about AIDS.

He meandered into the pool room. A couple of lads were playing, whilst a new face watched from his perch on a table. Mo smooched up and said hello.

'I ain't seen you round here before.'

'No's my first time.'

'I'm Maurice, but mostly Mo.'

'Trevor.'

'Got nowhere?'

'Sharing wiv me brother. But he wants me out. They're looking into it for me.'

'Who, Dave?'

'I think so.'

'He'll see you alright. Want to play pool?'

'Yea, why not.'

'Finished? Thanks. Grab a cue. What's your name.'

'Trevor.'

Mo set up the balls and decided he would break off, smashing them around the table. He was a frail man, looking ten years older than his forty-five. All the years of hardship had taken their toll. His hair was full and long, but pure white and the bones in his arms and fingers were harsh against his skin.

'Been in Coventry long?' he asked.

'Eight years. Since I was ten.'

'I've been here nine myself. Stayed in the old night shelter for thirteen weeks when I first came. Used to skipper a lot.'

'Where?' Trevor pocketed a spot ball, then missed one, but it blocked the hole, so he wasn't disappointed. He was finding it a bit of an effort though. Everything was these days.

'In tidy bins. Once, I woke up and was on my way to the scrapyard. I nearly didn't get out. I almost ended up in one of them metal crushers.'

'I slept rough a few nights.'

'Yea? Rough, ain't it. Not for me now.'

'On the streets. I found a shed in an old abandoned factory. It was like a hut. I didn't eat or drink nothing. Just had a couple of blankets, that's all.'

'I got used to it. I started off in Cardboard City in London.'

'Wha's'at?'

'It's a pavement where the homeless sleep out on cardboard and blankets. There were a hundred and fifty of us at times. The Sallie Ann used to come round. But there's a lot more youngsters like you there these days. I was there eighteen months. I didn't want to leave.'

'Why not?'

'It was the atmosphere. You know, mingling wi' people of your own ways. Everyone there had a problem. They were people you could talk to. You could talk to 'em. They were like meself. You know. I tell ya, there was a right mixture. Some people I saw there went on to become stars. People bought us food and clothing to tide us over, you know, keep us going. You got no folks?' He missed another shot. It was taking a long time to finish this game.

'Mum and two brothers.'

'What, left home, like?'

'Yea, we didn't get on.'

'Been anywhere else?'

'Salvation Army.'

'Long?'

'Six weeks.'

'Like it?'

'It was boring, all them old blokes living there.'

'Then where?'

'A mate's house in Radford. I shared his bedroom for five months. Then his brother came out of the army to live wiv 'is sister. We started fighting. So it was back to the streets.'

'Got no more friends?'

'They're all wiv their parents. I'm used to it anyway. I was in the Army Cadets.'

'Like them?'

'Great. Loved it. Learnt how to survive. But I didn't want to join the army.'

'What do you want?'

'I like farming a bit. There's a course at Barr's Hill school. I like animals. I like being outside. I did some painting once, but I don't like painting. Dad brought me up to look after myself.'

'What d'you do with yourself?'

'Go in caffs, that sort of thing. I was a mod. Got a Lambretta off a mate for three hundred quid. We'd sit in caffs and have a laugh. We'd do these scooter runs to Great Yarmouth or Morecombe. We'd be there for weeks, kipping on the beach or in sheds.'

'I bet you got some hassle.'

'Yea. Once there were two thousand of us. There were hundreds of police. They had this big fight. All these skinheads beat up the police.'

Mo finally knocked in his last ball and pocketed the black.

'Better go now. Got to see about the clothes. Want any clothes?'

'Nah, I'm O.K.'

'See ya then.'

'Yea.'

Mo pottered off back to the staff office. It was open now and he greeted the workers there. The office was chaotic.

'What's passing?'

'They're bringing the E.E.C. beef down soon. We're clearing out the back room to put it in there.'

'How much is there?'

'A ton. We'll have to put freezers in.'

'A ton. I'll pass the word.'

'O.K. Maurice, but we don't know when it's going out.'

'O.K., I'll keep quiet about it then. Any more news?'

'Coming to the meeting?'

'Of course.' He paused. 'Is the doctor coming?'

'Yes.'

'Hey, I want to open the clothes shop. There's a few new ones in.'

The worker rose, took the keys and went out to the cupboard where the donated clothes were kept. Mo went round and told everyone it would be open, then went back to distribute them. Not everyone got them. They had to be in special need. They were nothing marvellous, but, if a man had no coat or jumper, they could fit him out. Mo knew who'd had what recently and, as the clothes were sparse, was watchful in case someone came too often.

After an hour he closed up. The store was not very much, but it was a great help for some. He then went to queue up for a mug of tea. It was free and good. It was the only day centre for the homeless in the Midlands that was so cheap. Soup was free as well. Meals were 30p, plus 20p for a sweet and, if you wanted a shower or bath, you just paid for the soap. You could also get your laundry done for 60p. It was even worth the bus fare from Birmingham to eat here, because meals there were 80p and tea 15p. Norton House had a good reputation amongst the down-and-outs. It was very informal, except it was a dry house and didn't allow drugs.

He took his blue mug and sat at one of the dining tables in the small room. He sat on his own. He didn't want to talk to anyone, but wanted a bit of space. He thought about his life. His father had died of alcoholism before the War and, being the youngest, he'd had to cook whilst his mum was out working. Then, near the end of the War, he had joined the Army Catering Corps, then the Royal Army Service Corps, when he had been sent out to Burma. He had only been there two weeks and had never seen a Jap, when they were suddenly surrounded whilst brewing up some tea. The sergeant had told them to grab their rifles, but he had replied, 'Not on your nellie,' or words to that effect, and they had surrendered. The next ten months had been the horror of a Japanese prisoner-of-war camp, with no beds in the huts, all the mud and the dead left lying around. They had beaten his feet repeatedly with bamboo canes and he still limped from it.

He sipped on his tea. His chest hurt and he gave a deep, raucous cough. "All the smoking," he thought. That prison had shrunk his stomach and he could only eat small meals now. He never touched rice

94

either. He remembered the rats and cockroaches they had eaten. He pushed himself up and walked back into the hall. The weekly meeting of the members was going on in the front room, but he decided to miss it and climbed the stairs to the library. It was another average sized room. Norton House itself was a large house, aging, but with a modern extension on the back for the showers and toilets. He glanced along through the shelves and flicked a couple of love novels, before putting them back. He had trouble concentrating for long and his memory was playing him up, so he couldn't remember which ones he had looked at before. Reading was such an effort.

After the War, he had got a job on Southampton docks as a stevedore. His father had been one and the jobs tended to run in families. They used to drink a lot there, pilfering the odd bottle as they unloaded. There had been heavy drinking in the army as well. Then his wife had died of cancer.

He sat down in one of the old armchairs and quietly rolled another cigarette. He was in a funny mood. Contemplative. Remembering things he'd not for ages.

On the way to her funeral, all his four kids had been killed in a car crash. Suddenly, his whole family had been wiped out. He had hit the bottle spending £18,000 in eighteen months, losing his job and house, and ending up sleeping rough. He had got himself into a permanently dazed state, to stop all his worries and the desperate sense of the waste of his life, his own personal uselessness and guilt. He hadn't cared what he had drunk. In the morning, the first thing he had done was look for a drink. He had shoplifted to get enough money, but he had never begged. He still had his pride. Yes, most alkies still had their pride. There were things they would never do.

Drinking stopped the loneliness as well. Mo would share the bottles with his mates in the park or drink in a pub. But his problems were still there when he sobered up. Then the loneliness would hit him and the terrifying fear that he hadn't got a drink in case he needed one. Kids have teddies to talk to and be a comfort, he had his bottles.

He'd been to hospital twice for six weeks to dry out, but it hadn't done him any good. The money he had saved whilst in there had been spent straight away. They would sit outside Victoria Wines at 8.30 a.m. waiting for it to open, or hang around in Lady Herbert's Gardens, because it was near to Norton House and also Owen Owen's, which had an off-licence open all day. They would thieve from there, or from the Co-op.

A lot of blokes didn't want to give it up. He'd been perfectly happy to sit in a park, in the wind, rain and cold and to fall asleep, wet through.

He had been travelling for eighteen years. Firstly in Southampton, where he had just drunk and the only food he had had was the soup

95

handed out by the night van down in the park each night. Then he had gone to London, then up to Coventry. He'd slept in parks, in toilets, anywhere. He had tramped all over the country, sleeping in fields or under hedges, spreading some newspaper out over the top, or in hostels. He had thought of suicide many times and taken an overdose once, ending up in hospital for ten days.

When he had had a family and job, he had condemned people who slept out and swore he would kill himself rather than end up like them, but within four years, there he was. Everyone was potentially a down and out. Even now, after he had kept off the bottle for several years, he was only one drink away from being an alkie again. Always one away. He couldn't even drink coffee, because the taste reminded him of drink. Any drink did.

He had tried every way to get off before he had finally been successful. It was seeing the state of some of the people who had been down for much longer which had got to him. Their brains and bodies had just rotted away.

He finished his cigarette and looked around. A woman was sitting, snoozing in another armchair. All the furniture was old and well worn. That was why he felt at home.

He had tried antibuse to get off the drink. It had made him violently sick whenever he had taken a drink, but it had been too easy not to take the tablets. He had also been to the Coventry A.A., but hadn't liked it. They had always talked about how they got onto the drink, whilst he had wanted to be positive about life without drink. What had really helped was being with other blokes in the same boat. They had set up a group in Norton House. It was much more positive. It made him feel useful, helping others to get off it. He even talked to other groups and went to schools to chat about Norton House. He was going to speak to a group of ten kids from Henry VIII's, Coventry's public school, who wanted to hear how the other half lived.

He rose and sloped into the craft room. Gil and his brother Ray were in there with Frank, making a model of Norton House for an exhibition they were putting on in town. They had gone outside with a tape-measure and sized the dimensions, then constructed a model of it in cardboard and matchsticks, with little sofas, a pool table with two plasticine people playing at it and in the office was a minute typewriter, a table and even papers. Every room of the house was faithfully recreated and furnished. Also scattered around the craft room were other wooden artifacts. There was a guitar, bird boxes and wooden jigsaws.

Mo greeted Ray, who was painting a portrait of a woman, then waltzed over to Gil. He sat beside him.

'How's it going?'

96

'O.K. We're putting the light in.'

'The cathedral's good,' he said, inspecting that model. 'Got any more cushions?'

'Nah. They all went at the Foleshill Festival.'

'Done any more coaling?'

'Not recently.'

'A good number, that.'

'A fiver a day.'

'A bit early to start for me.'

'Yeh.'

Gil had been doing the odd job helping a local coal merchant. Each local colliery dug different coal. There was Baddesley, baker's nuts from Newdigate, Coventry large coal, Daw Mill, and anthracite and furnacite from the Homefire Plant. There was smokeless lighter, sunbright coke and many other types, all loaded into the bagging wagon to be dropped into hundredweight sacks, loaded onto the wagon and taken to the large bunkers of pubs and schools.

'Dinner soon,' Gil said.

'Yeh. Shepherd's Pie, then rhubarb crumble and custard.'

'You having any?'

'Yeh. Always do.' He sat again to roll another cigarette.

Twelve years he'd been on the road. Travelling, thumbing. Everywhere. Even Guernsey for a while, until they threw him into prison and boated him back. He would do odd jobs for farmers for a meal, like washing down the tractor or feeding the pigs. In every new town, it took some time to get his bearings, so he would head for the night shelter and stay there for a few days or weeks to get to know the place, suss out it and the people.

There were a lot of youngsters on the road now. A lot.

He pushed himself up again and casually crossed the landing and went down the stairs to get in at the head of the dinner queue. He had been in Winchester Prison numerous times for various offences, like shop-lifting, non-payment of fines and hitting a policeman. In there, he'd set up a little store. Mo's swap-shop, it was called. He had bought rings, pendants, fags, anything, and sold them again. He had even had his own bookies going. Baccy used to be the currency in there, but it was more often drugs these days. You arranged for the screws to pass you things. It had all been done by bartering. There had been a right market economy going on in there. He liked to think he had been a baron, paying half his takings to his bodyguards, who would go round, making sure people repaid loans, or paid up on payments for things they'd had. One thing he had definitely done was to make potato wine in the kitchens, using yeast and currents in with the potatoes, then hiding it in the fire extinguishers.

"Oh, yes," he thought. "I've been round the circuit. I've been in every institution going. From hospital to Cyrenians, to night shelter, to Sallie Ann, then back to hospital or prison. I've never settled. I've never been able to hold down a job. Anywhere permanent seems to hem me in. I'm restless, restless."

He had been down so many times, but now was on the up again. He was tidy and had decent clothes. He was proud of having improved his life. Also, for the last three months, he had had a relationship with a woman and that had restored a lot of his self-respect and confidence. He was in love with her.

The door of the kitchen opened and the woman who was serving started to dish out the dinners to those who had paid earlier. He passed a few jokes with those next to him in the queue. The atmosphere was always good in the house. Always. Yes, life was looking up.

City Final

98

THE OLD MAN

The old man sits
And bangs his pipe on the low wall,
Then sucks it to test the draw,
As he looks across
At the grocer serving bananas
To a young mother and child.
He scrapes and gouges the bowl
Clear of weeks of hardened ash,
Then blows and sucks and drags
'Til satisfied with the chill pull
Of the nicotine-flavoured air
Into his mouth.

Two young children
Play with bits of broken glass,
Glistening in the heat,
Laying them in patterns along the wall,
Kneeling before their
Little altar of stone,
Absorbed in the glinting crystals.

Reaching for his Virginia flake,
He carefully opens the tin
And rubs some of the golden brown
Between his fingers,
Presses it into the bowl
With a yellow-stained thumb,
Then strikes a match
Across the parapet
And sucks in the swirling threads of smoke,
As the light catches the tobacco.

It is hot on the wall,
The cars growling past
Making it sweatier still.
A woman leans in the doorway of the bookies,
Whilst one talks to a face
Sitting inside a Mercedes,

And another tries,
Without much luck,
To sell her body to passing trade.

He closes his eyes against the sun
And puffs gently
On the bitter smoke,
And relaxes and relaxes and relaxes.
Seventy years,
And the best days are these,
Sitting on the wall,
Without a care.

The giggling children,
Two girls,
Barely seven and eight,
Start sharing out the remains
Of bottles broken
By kids with bricks
And make a game from trash.

They stare, then one asks,
'Who are you?'
'Not who,' he replies,
'Not who, but what am I?'
And the girls return to their game
Whilst the man returns to his thoughts.

Behind him and a few trees,
A tall block rises up,
Its balconies decked in washing,
Open doors letting music
Permeate the air,
People lounging,
Drinking, snoozing,
Laughter, shouts, a slamming door,
A young woman screaming
As she is playfully chased
Across the balding grass,
Around trees with broken-off branches,
Through newspapers and chip-wrappings,
Until she's caught and tickled

Into submission.
A woman leans out

To shout for Marie and Tina
And the two girls rush off
For their lunch,
A lifetime of cares ahead.

Who am I?
Who am I, who am I?
Seventy years, and still I don't know,
Other than I shall never know,
Can never know,
Since too much is past and lost,
Too many memories forgotten or tinted
With years of reruns, edits and additions
'Til my memories have become
More real than reality itself.

I am too involved with my crises and ecstasies,
Too anxious for life,
Too occupied with what I must do,
To reflect upon what I am,
Or have become.

I ignore the ugly for the sake of sanity,
And hide beauty for lack of confidence,
And I am too concerned
With how I ought to live today
For reflection upon yesterday.
I am too much me to know me truly,
But that I have changed:
I am not the man I was an hour ago.

So what is this memory,
Memory upon memory,
What joys and what camouflages,
What penetrations of the unconscious?

I have been the shanty town man,
Back 'O The Wall's best mender of radios,
In the heat and poverty of Kingston;

I have been the Crossroads man,
On my apartheid bus to the apartheid park,
Sweeping under apartheid benches,
Laughing with black nannies pushing white's prams
They could never afford themselves;
I have been the Angolan peasant,
My hut burned by UNITA
And my son's legs blown off by a mine;
I have been the immigrant
Disembarking from Southampton,
Cheap wages and cheap conditions,
Turned away from the grimmest lodgings
Because of my colour.

And what am I now? I am an old man,
A happy old man,
Who know his hours of peace are here,
At last.

Down the hill, past the sweet shop,
The girls messing by the phone box,
The advert hoarding of a starving Ethiopian woman,
A child's doll discarded
And kicked around by some boys,
And the woman carrying a bag of shopping,
Trying to control a dog as well,
A few old ladies climb the steps
Into the bingo hall,
Leaving the doors swinging behind them.

Ah, memory,
Pain-kissing masseuse,
Soft shadows,
A blue sky of gentle imagining,
Caressed with sharp lightening strikes
Of guilt, missed opportunity
And loss.
Memory, which hides,
Which must be delved, questioned,
Connections be followed
And mysteries of lost experience recovered
In the surprise of sudden insight.

102

And what pains and pleasures
Has it yet to reveal?

What am I?
I am part of a world that is part of me
And cannot know me without knowing it,
No, nor change it,
Nor change me.

Ah, dreams,
Memories of dreams,
Mellow-merged into experience
And castigated upon realities.
Dreams,
Dreams which rose from necessity,
From inadequacies, lacks and needs,
From my search for answers,
Leading blind reality forward,
Defining it,
Lending it ears and eyes and a mouth
To scream its suffering,
And pulled back in their turn.

Why do we dream of plenty,
But that we experience want,
Why dream of happiness,
But that we are going through
Some kind of hell?
Reality is a dream,
Of how we perceive,
Of how we understand
Our need to live and strive for better things.
To dream is to control reality;
And, of dreams and reality,
Which, can I say,
Is the more true?

In the chip shop a woman serves schoolgirls
Who prefer scallops to school dinners,
And a woman doctor
From the health centre
Leads students

Training to be health visitors
To the minimarket
For apples and yogurt.
A dog chases its tail,
Barks at two old dears
Hobbling back from the shops,
Then yawns and returns
To curl under the dusty shade
Of a poplar tree.

'A Gathering' by Joanne Lewis

SIGNING ON

Graham arrived at the large, factory-like building at about twelve o'clock, went through a small side entrance and climbed several flights of dingy stairs, between yellow-washed walls. An old sign had a British National Party sticker on it, demanding immediate repatriation of the blacks.

He entered a large room with pink and beige washes and a row of four booths at the far end, behind three of which sat young women dealing with the queue of enquirers. They were each protected by a tough perspex and aluminium screen, with a steel mesh running along the top to stop any angry claimant vaulting this barricade and, Graham mused, perhaps strangling the beleaguered workers. It all seemed a bit absurd.

Down the middle of the room wandered a long queue of people waiting patiently for their turn at the enquiry booths. A large sign stated: "ALL CALLERS GO TO INQUIRIES", so he joined the queue. He looked at his watch. It was five past twelve. There were about thirty people before him, moving frustratingly slowly; hardly at all, it seemed. He realised he was better dressed than most of the people there, in a suit and coat. People were looking at him. He stood out. Already humiliated enough by the thought of the social security workers' attitudes, he hadn't expected these glances. The hot flush of embarassment swept over him.

At half one he was still standing in the queue. One of the workers had gone on her lunch break and put up a "POSITION CLOSED" sign, making progress even slower. He felt he shouldn't be claiming, because he at least still had nice clothes and a car. He wasn't as far down as these people, who'd obviously been unemployed for some time. He also dreaded meeting someone he knew.

A baby had been crying for the last half hour, the mother trying everything to quieten it as she stood in the queue. Another group, at the side, consisted of two women, a pram and two toddlers, all looking fed up and grouchy. A man was sitting, bottle-feeding another baby and in another row, there was a young couple with twin babies.

The queue wound its way between two blocks of bright orange bench seats, all firmly bolted down into the cream coloured lino on the floor. Fag-ends, used tissues, sweet wrappers and the odd empty can littered the floor. Overhead was one of those numbering machines, a left-over from the days when you took a ticket with a number on it and would wait for it to come up, saving you having to stand and queue for all these hours.

An oldish Asian gentleman was sitting quietly on one of the benches. Graham had already noticed that the young woman with a baby forced to sit next to him was trying to keep her distance, as if he had leprosy. There was unease on her face. A young bloke had been making audible comments about some fictitious smell for a few minutes. The man was obviously embarrased. Graham thought how loathe he seemed to be there, claiming benefit, how demeaning it seemed for him too.

The young man started on about filthy Pakis and the smell of curry. He then commented about the man's turban and, the next thing Graham knew, had tried to pull it from the man's head. There was a scuffle, then the young white let go and started grunting at him, calling him a Paki monkey, telling him to go back to the Paki zoo he came from and started making "Eeek, Eeek" noises.

'I'm not from Pakistan,' the man said.

'Oh, it talks. Grunt, grunt.'

'My brother is a doctor in Birmingham and my father was a high-ranking acountant with the government of the Punjab.'

This only fueled the abuse and the poor man was only saved by his name being called for his interview. As he rose, the man shouted:

'There he goes, bloody Paki, going to scrounge some more. I bet he's got fifteen kids to feed. They breed like f . . . ing rabbits. And all in one bed.'

A ripple of laughter followed the man as he disappeared. The woman moved up, visibly relaxing now he had gone.

The hall was packed. People smoking, the heat of bodies and radiators, plus the aches brought on by standing for so long, were making Graham irritable and frustrated. Not only him. A young man at one of the booths was getting very upset.

He had his benefit cheque in his hand and was waving it at the woman behind the perspex, shouting about why his benefit was being stopped. He was in bed and breakfast and had been there for months, but now the government's new rules about young people having to move on every six weeks had hit him and, in fact, thrown him out onto the streets.

'Where'm I supposed to live?' he screamed. The whole hall went very quiet. 'You lot don't give a f . . . ing shit. You don't give a f . . . if I'm on the bloody street or not. You're a bunch of shits.'

'I'm afraid we don't make the rules. We just carry them out.'

'Get me the people who make them then.'

106

'They don't work here. They're the government in Westminster.'

'Where's that?'

'London.'

'Don't give me any of that shit. What'm I going to live on? I can't live on that.' He threw the cheque at the screen. Then, in frustration, he jumped up onto the counter and tried to boot the screen in. The woman behind retreated, as did the other two and one went off to call the supervisor. The screen was impressively strong, because the man, about twenty, was over six foot and, in his denims and Doc Martens, obviously used to fighting. He banged the screen with all his force, but it still stayed in place.

The supervisor came and, instead of trying to calm him down, threatened him with the police. Perhaps he had no choice, but it made the man angrier. He climbed the screen and started to pull at the wire mesh above it.

The queue was surprisingly quiet. No one moved, except for the first few, who stepped back a yard or so. Some sitting with children were also anxious, but none wanted to lose her place. There was, Graham sensed, a sneaky sympathy for the man. Many of them had perhaps wanted to do that at one time themselves. Graham, having stood for over an hour, had felt like it as well. It was the unremiting effort to go and wait and explain and wait again and be constantly going back to get a little extra, or to enquire why some benefit had been arbitrarily stopped, or some change in circumstances. These were people for whom a few pounds was a question of life or death. The man was desperate. He was suddenly homeless and penniless, with a blank future of starvation suddenly staring him in the face and there were the people who'd done it, who knew nothing about his situation, who had never experienced it themselves, on whom he depended totally, but who had just cut him off. Pulled out his blood-line. They learnt quickly that being pleasant, patient and friendly to these government institutions didn't work. They simply forgot you. Some people had been waiting months for benefit cheques to come through, or for their rent to be paid, threatened with eviction, living off friends, or just forgotten. To get the pittance they could, they learnt to fight tooth and nail for it.

The young man had been sitting on the counter waiting for the police, both exhausted and confused about what to do. Then he stood up, unzipped his trousers and urinated over the screen, aiming under it, over the forms and papers on the other side. Then he started swearing and shouting again, until he jumped down and went round the side to look for another door to boot in. He found one and had a go at it, but it was locked. Then the police arrived.

They were quiet about it all. They restrained him, but spoke quietly and asked him to calm down. They wanted to know what it was all about and took him into a side room to question him.

The excitement over, the staff started to clean up the mess, reluctantly. It had only served to delay everyone for another half hour.

It was finally Graham's turn and he sat on the uncomfortable bench and peered through the perspex, waiting patiently whilst the woman behind finished writing down the details of the last enquirer. He explained his situation. He had just become unemployed. He had been self-employed and had had an exemption form from paying National Insurance, so he didn't think he would be eligible for unemployment benefit.

'Do you want to know what to do?' she asked.

'That would be helpful.'

'You have to go to the employment exchange.'

He sighed. All his queueing here had been a complete waste of time. He protested.

'But don't I have to fill in any forms here? I won't be entitled to unemployment benefit.'

'No. But you have to claim it anyway.'

'Even if I'm not going to get it?'

'Yes. You have to apply, then they'll say you can't have it and refer you to us.'

'But,' he said, 'I'm telling you now.'

'But you have to go there first. You'll have to sign on every two weeks anyway. You'll have to fill in a form to claim unemployment benefit.'

'Even though I'm not eligible.'

'That's right.'

'I think,' he said, 'I'm beginning to understand the system.'

'They'll give you a B.1 form. They'll make an appointment for you. Then you send that form here, after you've filled it in.'

'Haven't you got any I could take now?'

'We've got some, but you have to go there to get one. I'll find out which office you have to go to.'

She went off for a minute, then returned.

'Park Court,' she said. 'Go there and they'll give you a B.1 and make an appointment for you.'

He reluctantly faced the thought of another three hour wait and rose to go. Poor woman, he thought. She must see such poverty and despair, she must receive such abuse and so many desperate pleadings. The man who had been gasping and spluttering away behind him in the queue was replacing him at the booth. He was wearing an old greasy overcoat above a grimey suit. There was the stub of a cigarette in his mouth, a mere burnt remainder. Even sucking on that was better than nothing for him. Graham walked briskly past feet and stares, thankful to escape the heavy, choking air.

Instead of Park Court, in his inexperience, Graham was directed to the other employment exchange, at Cheylesmore. There, he was told that all names beginning with L went to Park Court and he drew a breath and traipsed off again. The rain was pouring by now and it seemed to set the seal on this miserable day. He trudged through the underpasses and streets to the large offices. Again, signs directed him upstairs, where he strolled over to the inquiries desk, relieved that there was only one in the queue. He was soon seen by a young woman, to whom he had to repeat everything in what seemed like his entire life story. 'Patience, Graham, patience,' he thought. In the section next to him, a lad was complaining that his giro hadn't arrived on Friday.

'It has probably been delayed in the post.'

'They've forgotten to send it.'

'It's in the post.'

'I phoned the D.H.S.S. up. They said they hadn't got it. What am I supposed to live on?'

'It's Christmas. It's probably been delayed in the post.'

'That's convenient. You always say it's in the post. What am I going to do? How am I going to live? Or buy anything? I could starve for all you care.'

'Ask the D.H.S.S. for an emergency payment.'

' I won't get one.'

'Well, I can't help you, I'm afraid.'

Suddenly, the young man exploded. He screamed and swore at her, banged his fist on the desk, then turned and stomped away, banging all the doors as the whole building was given the benefit of his disgust.

The woman dealing with Graham had been taking all that in her stride, busily filling in his form. She asked him when he wanted an appointment to sign on.

'Anytime. I've all the time in the world now, though you lot're using up most of it.'

'It'll have to be tomorrow now. We've no more appointments today. Will ten-thirty tomorrow be alright?'

'Fine,' he said, frustration seeping back. 'Fine, fine.' And he left for home, wondering precisely what he had achieved that day. He had been as meek as he could, hoping that passive co-operation would be the most energy-efficient and sanity-preserving way to proceed.

The next morning the place was packed. He sat in a corner to wait for his appointment. He was called five minutes early just for a change, again by a young woman. He wondered why they were all so young, speculating on the attrition rate. It must be a terrible job, acting as the smiling face of the daunting and bewildering bureaucracy surrounding the unemployed. They get it in the neck whilst the policy makers are insulated from the claimants and the hardship they suffer, glibly passing down memos and carrying out the often petty, penny-cutting schemes of the politicians.

He was given a purple B.1 form, on which there were a number of cunning catch-you-out questions, such as how much money were you prepared to accept for a job and how far were you prepared to travel to get work. Graham knew what they were up to. His previous slight distaste for the unemployed and nagging belief they were half to blame themselves for their situation was fast dissolving into a sense of solidarity. The questions were to encourage you to accept lower wages, for fear of pricing yourself too high and being disqualified from benefit. That was his fear, anyway. It was also a pressure to accept unskilled work.

The woman then gave him an orange and white signing-on card and another form because he had been self-employed. He was told to bring his accounts in for inspection, which he dreaded, not because they were a mess or a fiddle, but since a previous experience when the housing office, to sort out whether he was entitled to rent allowance, had kept them for three months and he'd had so much trouble trying to get them back. He was told to take the B.1 back to the D.H.S.S. and bring the other form back to Park Court. All this and he still hadn't officially claimed yet.

As he left the office, an old tramp was shouting and waving his stick at everyone who came out. He was harmless, but his ranting at the windows and brickwork summed up the madness of the world of the unemployed.

THE NOTICEBOARD

A new noticeboard had just been put up at the Crisis Intervention Centre. Annette, a worker there, had been given the task of pinning up all the notices and posters. It was a bright, new board, but the messages were depressingly familiar.

She pinned up one for C.O.V. – Care of Victims, a voluntary service for victims of robberies, muggings and such like. Then one for the M.I.N.D. Drop-In Centre and, in a top corner, one for the Coventry Family Conciliation Service.

Sometimes, Annette wondered whether this recent growth in charities, self-help groups and voluntary agencies was in direct response to the cuts in government services and the rising pressure caused by unemployment and low wages. They seemed to be filling the gaps, fingers in the dyke, with the stormy sea pounding away outside.

She put up a poster for the Alcohol Advisory Service in the other top corner, and one for the local Mothers and Toddlers Group under it.

Although society is affected as a whol), each person sees herself as an individual. She sees her suffering, naturally, in personal terms and feels it is her own fault or particular circumstance. Yet, from Annette's point of view, she could see things getting worse over the entire city. There was a great deal of anxiety, grief, pain and depression about. Some people were referred to them by doctors after they had taken overdoses. Sometimes, seeing a relation close to a breakdown, the family panicked and referred her to Walsgrave's psychiatric hospital. There she may in fact get worse, lose her identity and self-respect, or be labelled as "mad" or "neurotic". Annette had often been called up there. The vast majority were women who had simply had enough, had had a screaming fit, or had just broken down in tears, unable to cope. It was because women were still expected to be the carers, to take on others' problems and deal with them.

Up went a notice about Coventry Tranx Support for people on tranquilisers and another giving details of C.D.T., the Community Drug Team. Next to it, she pinned one for F.A.S., the Family Advisory Service.

At the hospital, she had to deal with the immediate crisis, calm the person, listen to her and try to find the real cause of the problem. People often repressed their feelings and tried to ignore them, but they still festered away. It was vital to normalise their feelings. A woman might be guilty at not having coped but who else would have? Why was it her fault when she had done everything she could? None of us were super-human. If it was a marriage crisis, they might never have talked about the problems, so Annette would try to get the husband in to talk. If it was the grandmother living with her, she would discuss with them how to cope and get them some social services support. Or her husband may have died and instead of feeling grief, she may feel relief. She might feel guilty at her abnormal grief pattern, but the marriage might have been awful and he might have suffered with cancer, or a series of strokes over the years and she feels glad it's all over. She might have been sexually assaulted by an uncle, which makes sex with her husband very difficult, but she feels it's her own fault, or that she encouraged him. She might actually have been raped some time ago and have kept it quiet, living with intense depression ever since.

Up went a notice for The Samaritans, another for Drinkwatchers and, in a prominent position in the middle, one for the Coventry Rape Crisis Centre.

Ten per cent of the population were admitted to a psychiatric hospital some time in their lives. They couldn't all be mad.

It was the pressures we all faced in life. It crossed all classes, although unemployment had had a significant effect in recent years. To most people, their families were the central unit of support. But when unemployment struck the financial and personal pressures mounted. A man might feel his life was a total waste, or a complete mess. Worries piled up. Or if a husband left his wife when the kids had grown up and gone, she was suddenly alone, with no one to care for and faced an "empty nest". There were also a few men, each usually in his fifties, whose wife had died or left, fed up with caring for him, who didn't know where to begin to look after himself and had no way of expressing his feelings at all. He may get psychosomatic illnesses, which were really a cry for help to be looked after again.

Annette just managed to squeeze a leaflet about the Valley House Association into one of the few spaces left. It said it dealt with "family breakdown, mental illness and personal crisis".

One in three marriages broke up. And what problems went repressed in those which didn't? The whole concept of marriage and the nuclear family was questionable. It was more an economic convenience than a social interpersonal one. Women were then tied down and, in this society, still lacked a lot of personal freedom. Their lives were totally for others, for their husbands and children, and they were left at home with the boredom and graft of repetitive housework and children.

So many problems of marriage lay unresolved as partners managed for a certain time, submerged in their work, but when the crunch came huge chasms suddenly appeared and the people concerned just cracked up. Usually, the person who was the biggest victim was the one who *could* see the problem, but it didn't suit the other, usually the husband, to face it. Men, she had found, were far less sensitive to others' needs. It was stereotyping from birth. They weren't expected to do any caring when they were children, or at school. As "husbands" and "breadwinners" they expected their wives to look after them. Oh, they were very good at talking about equality, but did very little about it. They still spent very little time caring for their own children.

Two more spaces were filled with a leaflet about drugs and another for relatives of drinkers. She also pinned up a card about an Old Furniture Collection Service.

The Centre was open every day of the year and staffed on a rota basis. Personal crises couldn't wait for Monday morning.

Counselling meant normalising the crisis, trying to work out the problems and finding solutions. She had to build a picture of the crisis, get to the root of it, help them over a period of months to cope with the problems, relieve them of their own guilt and get them to transfer it to the real guilty party, induce anger and rebuild self-esteem. Then if the person wanted, she could join a social group so she could meet people of her own age, with similar problems.

If necessary, the Centre offered up to seven nights' accommodation and, under a doctor, allowed medication, although that could be habit-forming and was not a long-term solution. It may be necessary to help people to sleep who were otherwise too upset to.

Annette pinned up the final notices. They were all for the positive side of self-help. One was announcing community classes at local schools, another explaining about literacy courses, then one about Adult Education classes and finally one for menopause self-help.

She could hear a phone ringing and expected she would be called to answer it. People's strength and resilience amazed her. Many faced so much despair, yet they climbed out of it and rebuilt their lives. In the final analysis, although she saw so much trauma, her job was rewarding in the help and new hope it gave to so many.

Valbert and Elam, at the Wood End demolition site, showing the "no fines" concrete walls.

THE END OF THE WORLD WILL BE ON FRIDAY*

It was Tuesday night, which for Jackie was the time she collected the pools coupons on her round. She had about forty which she visited early in the evening before it grew dark. She was trying to build the round up by knocking at a few extra doors each week. She would drop a coupon through each letterbox the week before, then go round and ask if they wanted to do them regularly. After taking the coupons, she would deduct her money for each one and post them the next morning.

She rang the bell on the first house. The man who answered was smartly dressed in an expensive, tan leather jacket, dapper trousers and highly polished leather shoes. His hair was in dreadlocks.

Jackie explained about the pools form.

'I remember,' he said. 'Come in.'

She saw his wife behind and agreed. She was shown into the living room.

It had a deep green dralon suite, dark brown carpet with a deep pile and had house plants everywhere. The woman asked her if she would like a drink.

'Coffee please.'

'We don't drink that. But we have chamomile tea or natural fruit juice.'

'Could I try the tea please.' She hadn't tried it before, so was a little reluctant. Also, Emmerdale Farm would be on soon and she wanted to know whether Amos and Mr Brierly would sort out the damage caused to their pub by the rioting protesters against the nuclear waste dump. It was all so terrible.

'By the way, my name's Grenville Davis. And this is my wife Rachel.'

'Jackie.'

He gently shook her hand.

'It's very nice in here.' She looked around the mirrors and wall units.

'Yes. I own a clothes shop in the city. I have another branch in Leicester.'

'Who's that?' Her eyes were on a painting of an old African man, surrounded with lions and set against a brilliant red and yellow sunrise.

'That's Haile Selassie.'

'Who's he?'

'Was he. He's no longer with us. He rose to Heaven after the agents of the beast, the Italians, invaded Ethiopia.'

Rachel, a black lady of about thirty-five and strikingly beautiful, brought in the drinks on a wooden try, inlaid with a picture of a man in dreadlocks. Taking his orange juice, Grenville explained that it was Bob Marley.

'Oh, I've heard of him. I love reggae.'

'He was a great man. He spread the message of Ras Tafari all over the world.'

'Who?'

'Ras Tafari was the King of Ethiopia and had the title King of Kings, Lord of Lords, Conqueror of the Lions of Judah. He fulfilled all the prophesies in the Bible about the second coming of the Lord. He *was* the Lord.'

'Do you believe in Jesus Christ and the Bible?'

'Of course. We follow the Bible to the letter. It's all in the Bible. All this present tribulation is foreseen. The Bible says the king will sit as a conquering lion. Haile Selassie could tame lions just by looking at them. They obeyed Him because they understood He was the Lord. There were the biggest crowds ever in Jamaica when He arrived at the airport.'

'But why do you wear your hair like that? There's nothing about that in the Bible. Jesus never had His hair in locks.'

'It *is* in the Bible. The Lord sayeth unto Samson not to shave the hair from his head. Look what happened when he did! It annoys me. The Lord Jesus is always seen as white. Jesu means "the black one". He was dark skinned. The Israelites were black people. The Jews aren't the true Israelites. They ruled a vast country stretching from Ethiopia and Egypt, over Arabia, to India. They were a great kingdom.'

'The Egyptians are brown, they're not black.' Jackie was getting confused by all this. Jesus being black was bad enough, but he seemed to be changing the whole of history to suit his beliefs. Also, she wondered if Jack Sugden had managed to hide the Chieftain tank he and Annie had captured from the army safely in the barn. It was a real cliffhanger.

'No, they were black at first. All the pharoahs were black, they were negroes. The sphinx had a negroid nose, but the Arabs knocked it off. The centre of ancient Egypt was Thebes, a black city. White historians have systematically destroyed all references to the great black civilisations, to fit in with their imperialist, expansionist, white, Christian morality.'

This daunted Jackie, who felt out of her depth. She tried to change the subject.

'Anyway,' she said.

'Oh yes,' the man sat up. 'I'm sorry. You must be a busy woman.'

'It's just I've got to see a few more people tonight.'

'I understand.'

'Do you want to do the pools for this Saturday?'

'There's no point.'

'Why not?'

'The world's going to end any day now. It might be in a year, or it might be this Friday. We've got our barrel together, our tent and sleeping bags and our passports, to dig up for Ethiopia when we're called.'

'Are you sure?'

'Positive.'

'But I'm supposed to be going to my mum's at the weekend.'

'All to no avail.'

'I'll have to cancel it, I suppose.'

'It's clearly written in the Bible. All the prophesies have come true. Scientists say it's six thousand years since Adam and Eve. God said He'd put man on this earth for six days and on the seventh, there shall be peace. One day is a thousand years. In that thousand years, Satan shall be bound. The Bible talks of a second coming of the Lord, this time as king. That was Haile Selassie, King of Kings, Lord of Lords, Conquering Lion of the Tribe of Judah. His throne was called the Throne of David.

'We see', he continued, 'wars all over the world and famine and disease. During this time, there will be four kingdoms in the four corners of the world, with winds blowing over the earth and sea. But a King will come from the east, who will hold back the winds whilst He seals the 144,000 chosen of the twelve tribes of Israel. The place they have to assemble is already prepared in Ethiopia. Some of our people have been there and seen it. Haile Selassie was a King from the East. He visited every important country and set up the Twelve Tribes of Israel in Jamaica. His body was never found. He just disappeared. There's no tomb for Him. The Bible says He ascended to Heaven.'

Jackie had a glazed look over her eyes by now, vaguely thinking of the time and of Eastenders at seven-thirty. Would Den and Angie get together again? It was the most important question to her, especially if the world was going to end. How would she find out? Perhaps she could phone up the television people and ask. She'd like to know, before everything ended. If she missed it tonight, there'd be trouble. But she had a certain interest in this man. He was the complete opposite of the Rastafarians she had imagined or heard about.

'Don't you all smoke cannabis?' she asked.

'No. That's a myth. There's nothing in the Bible about that.'

'Don't you see it as a natural herb, or something. Someone I knew used to smoke it because she said it made her more aware of herself, or something. It took away her cares.'

'I know many Rastas believe in the weed. But we don't,' he said looking at his wife.

'We don't drink alcohol either, do we Grenville,' she said.

'Why not?'

'It blurs the brain and leads to violence and unnatural behaviour.'

'And,' the woman said, 'we're strict vegetarians. Nor do we eat any preservatives or additives.'

'You must be very healthy.'

'We are. It's God's will. I smoke the weed at times, when I want to read the Bible and gain a greater understanding,' she admitted.

'We may eat the flesh of animals, but not the blood. God gave Noah all the herbs and animals for meat, but not their blood or fat. Their blood must all be drained out.'

'We take the prophesies heavily unto ourselves,' Rachel said. 'We take our religion seriously, though it's very difficult to live up to it in this Babylon.'

'I thought Babylon was in Egypt somewhere?'

'No. It means everywhere outside the chosen land, but especially the centre of evil, the United States and England. But the Catholic Church is the organisation of the Antichrist. It is the agent of the Beast which rules Babylon. The leaders of the Church are demons, making people worship on heathen days. They are making people worship the Devil. Their priests are witches, obiah workers, pretending to teach about Jesus Christ, only to deceive. The Pope has a lot of power and uses it very deviously. He is working for the beast. One day, the Devil will announce himself King of the World.'

'The Vatican tried to kill Haile Selassie. Mussolini was carrying out its wishes when he invaded Ethiopia,' Rachel said.

'That's right.'

'I think the Freemasons are the real agents of the Devil,' she added.

'Now they're considering women priests, but that is an abomination in the House of the Lord. It's all to do with the Italians. It was revealed that the Beast would have a scarlet woman on its back. That woman is the Church. It's secretly marking everyone with 666 on their foreheads.'

'We don't have a proper church to tell us what to do. We don't believe in that. We have meetings of the Twelve Tribes, but there's no writs or rites, just an inward co-operation of one's heart. Twelve men and women stand at the front, each in the colours of their tribe.'

'Each tribe has a colour?' Jackie asked.

'Oh yes. When were you born?' Grenville inquired.

'March.'

'You'll be a Benjamin then. The colour of that tribe's black. And your part of the body is the foot. Benjamins are very intelligent. I'm Simeon. That's supposed to be cruel, but it's only a tendency.'

'Do you have services?'

'No, we have witnessing,' the woman replied.

'What's that?'

'People come to the front and tell how they've experienced the prophesies and say what they think we should all do to prepare.'

'Soon, we're all going to dig up and go to Ethiopia. We're just waiting for the sign.' Grenville drank some more of his orange juice.

'What, all of you?'

'Yeh. Quitting Ephraim – England to you – escaping the Antichrist and the influence of Rome. We're leaving the evil and going to the chosen ground. Jesus will come with seven angels, blowing trumpets and all the 144,000 will join Him on a cloud. All true believers will be raised. Four of the trumpets will sound and smite parts of the earth and man. Then everyone will have the chance to repent, because the last three trumpets will be worse. Then they will sound and all the horrors will descend. Then Satan will be bound and Jesus Christ will descend to the earth for a thousand years and teach us about God and belief. After that time, Satan will be released and make war. God will send down fire and brimstone and destroy everyone. Then God will come with the Judgement Book and every single person shall be raised. That's the second resurrection.'

'There'll be two?' She was starting to panic. Eastenders was getting close. She'd given up on Emmerdale Farm. But it was Dallas night as well. Pam had had another dream and she wondered who else would return from the dead. Apart from Jock, that was. Last week, two more people turned up claiming they were the old man. One was a woman who said she'd undergone a sex-change operation and one was an eighteen year old hippie on L.S.D.

'Yes,' Rachel interrupted. 'Then all those not in the Book will be thrown into the Lake of Fire. Satan and his false prophets will burn for ever and ever, but flesh will die in the Lake.'

'Nasty.'

'Israel is riven with wars. Jerusalem has been smashed down and reduced to rubble. Revelation,' she continued, 'even talks of the nuclear. There will be wars and tribulations, the moon will turn to blood, the stars will fall to the earth and the sun will darken. That's what'll happen after the nuclear.'

'The signs are everywhere,' her husband said dourly. He had reached over for the bible earlier and been flicking through it.

'It's all here,' he said, and proceeded to read to her Acts, Chapter 2, Verses 29 to 32, Acts, 13, 20 to 23, Romans, 9, 33, Corinthians 1, 5 to 8, 1 Timothy, 6, 14 to 16, Hebrews, 9, 28, Revelation, 3, 10 and 17, 14, and 18, 4, and 19, 10 to 19.

Jackie was trying to find an excuse to leave, but couldn't get a word in. If it all ended on Friday she'd miss the omnibus edition of Eastenders on Sunday, so she had to see it tonight. And the omnibus of Brookside on Saturday. She would never know if Sheila and Bob split up, or if

119

Damian's ex-girlfriend would have an abortion. Why couldn't God wait until next week?

'I must be . . .' she mumbled.

'Grenville, show our guest the sculpture.'

'Oh yes. You see,' he said, rising and picking up a bronze head of Haile Selassie to show her, 'Rastafarianism isn't a religion really. It's finding out who you are, where you came from and where you're going. There's not a church, in the sense of buildings and priests, only in the sense of the family of Christ. It's a culture, with paintings and music and art and ways of living and dressing. I don't hold with transplants nor blood transfusions either. I think I would have to lie there and die if I was in an accident.'

'We believe in the Earth. God is the Father and the Earth is the Mother. We are still in Her womb.'

'We're not truely born yet.'

'No, praise the Lord.'

'Do the police bother you?' Jackie asked.

'The police are the agents of the beast. They deliberately incite us with taunts about Haile Selassie being a homosexual and saying they'll cut off our locks. 999 is 666 upside down, in'it? We aren't violent by nature, but Jesus said we can only take so much. There is an end to what any man can suffer. But some police like the Twelve Tribes of Israel because we abhor violence. They see our role as peacemakers.'

'We say "One love" when we greet, you see.'

On the coffee table was a bible. Grenville kept patting it and glancing through it as he explained the prophesies. He told Jackie about Adam and Eve, the Garden of Eden and the Flood, about Abraham, the twelve sons of Isaac who fathered the twelve tribes, about the exile in Egypt, Moses, Saul and David, about the twins of Judah, about how Jeremiah escaped to Egypt, and how the true throne of David came to Ethiopia.

Jackie was in a state of high tension by now. All she could think about were Angie and Den. She rose during the last speech, somewhere between the seven plagues and the parting of the Red Sea. She made for the door, being as polite as she could and was equally politely seen away.

She decided she had just enough time to quickly knock a few more doors but, as the next door opened and she was invited in, she noticed a copy of "Watchtower" on the hall sideboard. She turned and fled.

* With thanks to Valbert McCook

120

THE WEST INDIAN LUNCHEON CLUB

Amy opened the tins of ackee and tore open the bags containing the salted ling fish. She then dropped the fish into a pan of water, before she started to peel the skin from the still-frozen flesh.

Bernice washed the rice in a pan. She melted a block of coconut, added a sprig of thyme and the rice, boiled some brown gongo peas, finely diced an onion and added them as well.

Amy started on the green bananas. She slit the ends and split each along its back, washed it, peeled off the skin, scraped off the excess peel and washed it again.

Bernice checked the rice and peas, whilst getting the suet flour and salt together for the dumplings. She mixed them together, adding water and then pulled and squeezed them into squashed ball shapes. Once finished, she put the salted fish on to boil.

Amy took a piece of white yam and a piece of yellow, started to peel them and put them into salted water to boil. She was careful of the yellow yam, because it was itchy to the skin.

Bernice poured a little vegetable oil into a large frying pan. She had chopped some onions and now added them to the oil, putting in some pepper and thyme for good measure. She stirred it until the onions were brown, then poured in a tin of tomatoes. After a few minutes stirring, in went the yellow ackee and the fish, which had already boiled for a few minutes. She shook in a good deal of white pepper and gave it all a good stir.

Dorothy during this time, was helping clear and arrange the tables in the dining area. The other half of the large room of the day centre for the elderly had a number of easy chairs arranged in a semi-circle about a small colour television. In the seats, a few West Indian elderly and a young black woman with her baby were sitting.

Amy opened the wrapping of the bowl of cold cornmeal pudding she had made the day before. It contained sweet potato, coconut, sugar, nutmeg, mixed spice and salt. She had grated the sweet potato, kneaded it, added the flour and spices, a little milk, then mixed it and put it in to the oven for three and a half hours.

Bernice put a load of already cooked chicken wings into another frying pan, added onions, thyme and a tin of tomatoes and let that simmer as well. Then she and Amy sat down to have a chat about the church meeting on Sunday.

They had a full week, both of them, carrying on the work of their church as they felt they should. Bernice was one of its evangelists, whilst Amy helped out in other ways, cooking occasionally for some elderly people at the Church of God on Tuesdays, taking Mrs Grant to get her pension on Wednesdays and doing her cleaning for her on Fridays and of course, cooking for the West Indian luncheon club on Thursdays.

She had arrived in England in 1961 from Santa Elizabeth in Jamaica when she was twenty-one. Her three brothers had come over as well. She had worked at a cotton mill in Manchester, spinning and threading the bobbins and weighing them if they ran short. Then she had gone to live with her brother in Hertfordshire and had worked as an auxiliary in a hospital, before coming to Coventry with another brother and working at the G.E.C. on a capstan operating machine, making parts for televisions. She had also screenprinted the circuit boards there, before the boredom had driven her bananas and she had left.

After that she had worked for the Midland Red buses, cleaning them and making tea for the drivers. They had been nice people, but after two years she had lost interest. Courtaulds had then taken her on as a processor, running the yarn, in a process similar to spinning. It had been a big machine with big bobbins called cheeses, threaded through from the back. It had been a new machine and the conditions had been good.

Last year she had worked for the Blue Board Café at Watford Gap on the M.1, cleaning the toilets and dining hall at night, picking up a coach each evening from Coventry's Pool Meadow bus station.

So, quite a life, she thought, glancing around at the pans bubbling gently away.

Bernice looked at her watch.

'Come on,' she said, 'it's time to serve up the feast, don't you think?'

'I do,' Amy replied and the two ladies set about dishing the lunches out.

THE ST BARNABAS CENTRE

As the Reverend David Thomas walked briskly past the factory next to his church, he noticed the Community Transport minibus on the drive outside the church's community centre. He ran up to help the old people out.

'Good morning everyone. Ah, Mr Cheema, how are you?'

The elderly Sikh gentleman clambered cautiously down. He smiled back at the young vicar.

'Let me help you in. Morning, Anita. Morning, Jean. Hello, Mr Singh. That's right, Mr Cheema. Watch, there's a puddle there. That's it. Now a step. In through the door. That's better, isn't it. A bit warmer in here. Watch the door. Mind. That's right. Where would you like to sit?'

Mr Cheema, who was blind, mentioned that he didn't mind where he sat, but David Thomas knew he had a favourite armchair, guided him to it and helped him sit down.

The other Asian elderly, about six in all, were slowly coming in from the February cold to sit around the warm chairs of the family centre. Viro, one of the workers there, placed a jigsaw before one man and took out some weaving materials for making baskets.

David sat and talked with Mr Cheema and Mr Singh. They talked about the Coventry Interfaith Group. David saw this as a vital part of his role as a Church of England vicar. His was a small parish, tiny in fact, but covering an old, inner city area which had a large percentage of non-Anglicans, either from India or Ireland. His pastoral role had to be for all faiths. It had to confront the issues of unemployment, racialism and a deteriorating environment. As the community paper, which was delivered free to every household every month pointed out, Coventry had 1,700 homes unfit to live in, 2,400 people in urgent need of accommodation and 10,000 on the council waiting list. The thing was, not to moan about it, but to get people off their backsides and doing things, to build on the community and restore people's faith. That was the positive way, the only way, to cope with such conditions.

David rose and asked everyone if they wanted tea or coffee. Four teas and two coffees. He went off into the kitchen to make it. Anita was in there with Harvinder, preparing the food for dinner.

'Smells delicious.'

'It's okhra and lentils today, with curried cauliflower, potatoes and japatis.'

'I'm making the coffee.'

'I'll make it,' Anita said.

'No, you get on with your list, whatever it is. What is it?'

'The activities for the week. You know, bingo, a beetle drive, a slide show.'

'A slide show?'

'Yes. For the pensioners. Mrs McCarthy took some slides of her trip to Paris last summer, so we're showing them.'

'Where' the teabags?'

'Up there.'

'And we're having another noisy quiz on Friday.'

'How's the women's health group coming along?'

'Fine. We had twelve last week.'

'And has the mums and toddlers group picked up?'

'No. We just can't seem to get that going.'

'Perhaps there's something about the hall they don't like.'

'I think we need a good mum who knows all the others to get it going.'

'How'd the swimming trip go?'

'That was a great laugh. There's the sugar. One for me, two for Harvinder.'

'The Asian women's group's picking up,' Harvinder said, stirring the large saucepan of curry.

'Good, good. I'll just take these through. Phew, it's busy today. I've got to check those hymn books which need replacing. Did G.E.C. give anything for the raffle?'

'They were very good. We got a box of tins.'

'Oh, David,' Jean said, coming into the kitchen, 'we had a problem with the shower when we used it for Mrs Simpson yesterday. It's leaking.'

'How is she?'

'She had a visit from the health visitor on Monday. Apparently, she's not been able to get up her stairs for weeks, so they've moved her bed downstairs. She's cheered up a lot these last few days.'

'I'll make sure I visit her. Right. Teas and coffees. Excuse me.'

He carried the tray back into the sitting room and distributed the drinks, then sugared Mr Cheema's for him. He left and went through the foyer to the hall. Veena and Alison were there, running the playgroup. Alison had made some toast for the three and four year olds, some of whom came in without having breakfast. She said hello to David and asked permission to put up a notice asking the parents to make cakes for a cake stall. He, of course, agreed, pleased that the mums were being encouraged to get involved in the centre. The parents had to pay for the children, but the playgroup was charity run so, if a family was finding it difficult, as some were, it was alright to miss the occasional week.

The vicar then went through the door in the large glass wall between the church hall and the church itself. It was a small place of worship, plain, unassuming and quiet after the bustle of the family centre. He went over to the cupboard where the hymn books were kept, opened it and took some of them out. As he sat down in a pew to inspect them, his mind started to question his role there. At times, there seemed so much to do and so few resources to do it with. And then, some of his parishoners argued that he should spend more time on traditional, anglican duties. Some didn't see the family centre as of value in its own right, but more of a recruiting ground for the church.

David saw his role as serving the whole community and enabling it to develop its own capabilities. His congregation was tiny, under one per cent of the parish, so his role had to be wider. When he'd been a curate in Kirkby, a large Liverpool housing estate, he'd been chairman of the tenants' association which had fought to improve the appalling conditions of broken lifts, flooding in the flats, vandalism and rubbish left uncollected for months. He had lived in one of the flats himself and a common experience led to a common understanding and desire for change.

He placed those books with broken spines or ripped pages to one side, then stored the good ones again and took out another batch.

The church was small and quite recently built. It had no glorious stained glass windows or ornate carvings. It was simple, peaceful and excellent for its purpose, the worship of God.

The Church was written off by radicals. Yet he was a radical himself and he believed it provided a very important support network for single women, the elderly and others who perhaps had no other social outlets like clubs or pubs. But he firmly rejected the idea that the Church was merely a safety net for the most vulnerable in society, as though there was something wrong with that. It was as legitimate a meeting place as any other.

He felt everyone needed to fundamentally reappraise the way they thought and viewed others. The Church and society in general had a very paternalistic attitude to the poor. It was all charity from above, forcing the poor to become dependent on the better off, to feel lesser, unequal, like the appalling queues for E.E.C. butter and milk. So many people thought that going to church once a week was good enough for God. Those who took part in Live Aid were like that. Sure, it was marvellous that it raised interest and money, but people were doing it for their own gratification and because it was hyped into an attractive, exciting thing to do. There was a lot of baloney talked about running for famine, because most were running to have a good time. It was the old hand-out mentality.

He stretched and rose up. The church was cold and he walked towards the pulpit to get the blood flowing in his legs again. He climbed up the steps and glanced at the open bible, still set at last week's lesson about the meaning of the Good Samaritan. He rested his hands on the pulpit and, for a moment, remembered the times his church had been full, occasions when the whole community, regardless of creed, had gathered together.

The poor must be treated as equals. They must be encouraged to develop their own skills, learn to look after themselves, fend for themselves, and value their own attitudes.

Many people in the church assumed that Christian values were middle-class values. Notions such as thrift, honesty, self-denial, gentleness and "love for your neighbour" were seen as the unique preserve of the middle class. Yet nothing could be more false. The practice of sharing, loving and caring was much more evident in areas like Hillfields and Foleshill, as well as in the traditions of parts of Africa and Asia.

There was a need for a change of attitude in the Church. It was seen as a profession, a career, by some and thus tended to draw its hierarchy from the middle class, sons of clergymen and public schoolboys. People often expected those middle class values from him. It wasn't just the Church of England either. The Non-Conformist churches had become a lot more bourgeios in the last hundred and forty years, dominated by middle class values and social aspiration.

He remembered he had a meeting of the Youth Panel of the Community Relations Council to attend the next day and had to prepare a report. It woke him from his gaze and he turned back down from the pulpit, back to his pew and hymn books.

Take racism, for example. There was no way you could abolish racism from above, by decree. Racism could only be combated by treating all races as equals. He had three Sikhs and an Afro-Carribean working at the church centre, which was a very positive statement about the value every group was making to the community. They held race awareness sessions to overcome ignorance and implicit racial attitudes. His role on the board of governors of the local Stanton Bridge Junior School was similar, to ensure there was a multi-cultural education offered, since ninety per cent of its pupils were from minority groups and to make sure the religious traditions of the school were maintained. Coventry, he felt, had a very strong commitment to multi-cultural education. It had a good record. He'd seen all the progress that had been made. He'd seen the Foleshill Festival develop into a whole series of events. He'd convened the Foleshill Interfaith Group and visited temples for festivals such as Diwali and Eid and was chairman of the Foleshill Fieldworkers' Forum, which was there to raise the understanding of ethnic groups by professional workers in the community, amongst other activities.

He looked at his watch. It was nearly half-twelve, the time he had agreed to meet the Methodist minister at the Catholic Club for a game of pool. He put away the remaining good books and carried the others out with him.

'I wonder how the Arsenal'll get on against Spurs next weekend?' he murmured. He'd ask old Harry. Harry liked to talk football. That was the way to his heart and to his mind. If you knew about football, Harry'd listen to you talk about anything else. Now, with his wife Flora, it was baking. She was shy and he had not been able to get under her guard until one day she'd brought out her Christmas cake and they'd talked about sponge mixes and puff pastry. Since then, she had really opened up to him.

That was his role, drawing people out of their isolation and bringing them together to share with each other. Apart from glueing hymn books, that was.

THE INTERVIEW

Winston entered the office of the wholesalers. The secretary, a middle-aged woman, gave him a cursory glance, as if to say he shouldn't be there, then indicated upstairs in an equally off-hand manner.

He went up and cautiously entered the waiting room. A young white girl was sitting in a chair in one corner and, in another, sat his old friend Daniel.

'Hey man,' Winston said. 'What you doing 'ere then?'

'I've got an interview. You O.K?'

'Fine man.' They slapped hands and shook.

127

'You're looking smarter than a cat's arse there, Winston.'

'I've come for that warehouse job.'

'Snap, man.'

'You too?'

'Sure thing.'

'I thought you were on a Y.T.S. course,' Winston said.

'I jacked it in. I dug up months ago.'

'Why's that then?' Winston sat down beside him, tucking his tie into his belt. 'You were dead keen on it. You said it was proper training, not the usual crap. Double glazing, weren't it?'

'Yea. Promised me a bonus after six months, didn't they. An' promotion.' He looked over at the white girl, who was pretending not to listen to their conversation. 'It was a real good number, proper supervision, everything. I was good at it an' all. Learning how to fit the windows together, seal them, things like that.'

'So, what happened?'

'Me black face didn't fit, did it.'

'Same old story.'

'You got it, man. Someone in the warehouse got sick, so they said I had to fill in.'

'What, full-time?'

'Only 'til he came back, they said. I said I was supposed to be doing the windows, but I 'ad no choice. They cut me wages an' all.'

'Shit.'

'After a month, nothing happened. "When's this guy coming back?" I asked. They never said. Then they took on this white guy on Y.T.S., doing what I was doing, so I got the message. Great, ain't it. An' I was getting all the stares and looks and racist jokes. "Come on nigger, lift up them boxes," and all that, you know.'

'So you jacked it.'

'I felt pig sick, man. I dug up one day and told 'em where to stick it.'

There was a pause. Both lads looked over at the girl. She was hiding behind some magazine or other. A frail girl, barely out of school, by the looks of her.

'Ain't you done no Y.T.S. yet?' Daniel asked Winston.

'They 'ad me down for one with some charity. But there weren't no future in that. Then I got one over at Tile Hill College, doing computers. It was O.K., but no chance of a job. I was doing my workplace experience in the office of a little company. They hardly let me near their precious word-processor. It was all filing and errands.'

'Yeh, they say it's training, but it ain't.'

'Me mate Asif got a Y.T.S. placement doing his City an' Guilds in car maintenance. D'you know where they had him working?'

'Nah.'

'Valeting cars.'

'Baz Johnson was doing his City and Guilds in woodwork and he was made to do self-assembly kitchen units. They had him working some circular saw or something, without supervision.'

'Why do we bother? There ain't no point.'

'They just exploit us. It's cheap labour for 'em. About a tenner a week, it costs firms, that's all. They don't pay no national insurance neither.'

'They're racist anyway. We get the worst schemes. You know, whities stand twice as much chance of a job at the end of a Y.T.S. than we do.'

'It's keeping us off the unemployment figures. Keeping us quiet.'

'They don't want us to join no unions neither. We're just scivvies without any rights.'

'An' some've got the nerve to ask for 'O' levels, man. Entry requirements to be a slave.'

'Yeh, but some kids think it's great. Get on a Y.T.S. at the Jag or a bank an' you're made.'

'We don't get them, though, do we.'

'No chance. It ain't proper training. It's all skimping. Superficial. All semi-skilled. It's just getting us off the street.'

'They put us in a supermarket and have us filling shelves or on the check-outs. What skill's that?'

Their conversation was cut short by a woman entering the room. She briefly introduced herself and explained about the interviews. She kept looking at the two black lads. When she had finished, she disappeared for a minute, then came back.

'Daniel Demoussins, can you come with me?'

Daniel rose and followed her into the interview room, straightening his tie and making sure the jacket of his suit was buttoned.

The two men behind the desk in the room politely offered Daniel a chair.

'Ah, Daniel. Yes. We. . .er. . .your C.V. is quite impressive. Four C.S.E.s. School report's fine. Hard worker. Done some voluntary work, I see . . .'

'Yes,' Daniel said, 'gardening for the old folks in Stoke Aldermoor.'

'But,' asked the other man, leaning forward, 'have you had any experience in a warehouse before?'

'Yes, a bit, on a Y.T.S. scheme.'

'That's not really what we were looking for. You see, we wanted someone with enough experience.'

'The advert said unskilled.'

'Yes, Mr. . .er. . .Den. . .'

'Demoussins, sir. But how much do you need for warehouse work? My experience taught me you don't need any experience.'

'Yes, but, as I was saying, there's unskilled and there's unskilled.'

The remark totally baffled Daniel. The first man asked him about his hobbies. Daniel was again thrown. What about the job, he thought. But he listed them and watched a glazed look rapidly spread over the two men's eyes, as they both avoided looking at him.

'Thank you, Mr. Demoussins. That will be all for now. Thank you for coming. We'll be letting you know.'

As he was shown back, Daniel knew exactly what had happened. Once the secretary had reported back that he was black, he had lost the job. He sat back next to Winston, as the young girl was shown in.

'How'd it go?'

'F. . .ing hobbies. Had I any experience? There's unskilled and unskilled!'

'A waste of time?'

'Again. Why do we bother, eh? All we get's hassle. I might as well've stayed at home. This *always* happens.'

'Not a chance?'

'Going through the motions. They couldn't even look me in the eye, they were so bloody embarrassed. They knew I'd sussed them out. It pisses me off. They don't give a damn, so long's they don't take on no nigger-man.'

'This country's got to me, man. It supposed to be ours.'

'This ain't my country. Them honkies don't want us an' we don't want them.'

'Don't let it get to you, man.'

'All my pissing life, I've taken this. Even when I was little.'

'Just get used to it. Psyche them out. You got to be laid back about it, man. No use letting it get to you. I'm proud of being black.'

'School was the same. All white history. Africa and China don't exist for that lot. Who cares about glaciated valleys in Scotland in a class full of black kids, man?'

'I never knew we were all from Africa 'til I watched "Roots". My mum whipped me when I told her. "We ain't no Zulus," she screamed. She got the thickest belt out to me.'

'It's all denying our culture, in'it.'

'I've been on five different courses now,' Daniel said, 'and they ain't done me one little bit of good. Soon's they sees my face, that's it. No contest, man. Might as well swing 'round the lampshades for half an hour.'

'They say Y.T.S. ain't racist, but it is.'

'White T.S., in'it.'

'We used to get put on them B schemes all the time.'

'You don't see no black Y.T.S.ers up the Jag or Masseys or the Alvis, do you. Not on the best schemes, not where you get a decent job at the end. It's all them little places with no unions and no proper supervision, where they take one lot of Y.T.S.ers after another for cheap labour.'

'It's blowing my mind, this country. It's going to the dogs. That government's the devil. It's evil, man. We've got no jobs, so we can't buy no houses, so we get dumped in Hillfields or Wood End, or Willenhall, all on social, all degraded, all lumped together as lazy scroungers and thieves.'

'I ain't surprised so many brothers don't try no more,' Daniel added.

'I had one interview where the manager said he'd like to take me on, that I had the best qualifications and experience, but he didn't think I'd fit in. He didn't think I'd enjoy working there, because I'd be the only black guy and I'd get picked on. I wouldn't like it and it'd be too much trouble for them, so it was best all round that I didn't get it. Wished me well, the bastard.' Winston was incredibly bitter. 'We're all treated like aliens here. They think we're all monkeys or slaves.'

'I can't take all this pressure on my head.'

'I don't check for this equality jive. We ain't never going to be equals in this country.'

'We live in them tower blocks, so many people stacked on top of each other, no room to breathe, miles from the country. We ain't got no cars to go out and see the trees and smell the fresh air. You wonder why there's so many suicides, man? Or all the crime? Or everyone digging up and moving out all the time? It's the pressure, man. Women on their own with kids, or old people living in the greatest dread, loan sharks stealing their money, it's damn well frightening, everything.'

'We should all dig up.'

'It's too crowded, man. We're all hemmed in. Like battery chickens. It's so depressing, man, all that pressure on your head.'

131

They heard footsteps and the door opened. The girl walked straight through, whilst the woman talked to the two lads.

'I'm afraid we won't need to interview you, Mr White.'

'Why not?' Winston asked.

'We've given Miss Hains the job.'

'What, lifting heavy weights in a warehouse? How can she be...'

'We don't believe in stereotyping people,' the woman said.

'Just us.'

'Leave it out, Winston,' Daniel said. 'You know it ain't no use. Come on. Let's get out'a here. This place stinks.'

'Dave and Kenny Thompson, fishing in the
Coventry canal.

OF HAMMERS AND SHOVELS

Rex and Seamus measured up the size for the box, first its length, then its width. They went over to a pile of three-quarter inch ply and started to sort out enough pieces of the right shape for it.

They were chippies, working on a multi-story office block in the town centre, and the box was for part of the next floor being built. It was constructed section by section. Firstly, the steel fitters made up the steel rods into a cage bound together by strong wiring, for the pillars. This frame was securely wired onto the protruding ends of the steel bars of the pillars from the floor below. In their turn, they were long enough to stick out above the next floor. Next, it was the chippies' job to make a box mould for the concrete to be poured into. That was easy. All the pillars were standardised, so the four side-sections of one box could be taken off by wrenching out the nails and hammering them off the set concrete on one pillar and simply reassembling them for the next.

It was all simplified and standardised. That way, it was fast and efficient. After the boxes for the pillars were made, the concrete was poured in from a large bucket suspended from the crane. Half-a-dozen or so pillars were done first, then, when they had hardened up, the boxes to contain the floor beams were constructed and the floor itself was laid, section by square section, on top of the beams.

Rex was English, from Durham, whilst Seamus was, of course, Irish, from County Wexford. They worked as a team, sorting the plywood and nailing it up.

Nearby, a West Indian man was working. He was a labourer, unloading some breeze-blocks from a wheel-barrow, before pushing it off to get some more.

Rex hated people whose skin happened to be black. It was a deep-rooted resentment at them being in 'his' country and merely the sight of one angered him. He disliked gays and 'looney lefties' as well, though he was a solid Labour voter and had been so since he'd first voted for Wilson in '66. Having to work near a black person really started him off.

'What,' he asked Seamus, 'do you get if you cross a wog with an octopus?'

'What?'

'A first-class cotton-picker.' He mixed this story with a flood of abuse, making certain it was loud enough for the labourer to hear.

'Hey, Rex,' Seamus taunted him, keen to keep him going, 'Wha's 'is I hear about your daughter marrying a darkie?'

'Not likely. I'd never let 'er in the house if she did, and she knows it. I don't believe in them black an' white minstrels.'

Though Irish, Seamus didn't feel so much a foreigner as he felt the West Indian was. He was glad to be able to side with Rex against someone else for once, instead of being the butt of his Irish jokes.

'A bloke went to a hospital for a transplant,' Rex said, loudly. 'After the operation, the doctor said, "I've got some good news and some bad news. The bad is your new liver's from a West Indian and your blood's from a Paki, but the good news is, your ding-a-ling's grown five inches and you've gone to the top of the housing list".'

Immediately on its heels came another.

'A wog was walking his duck along the road. This bloke comes up and says, "That's a nice pig you've got there." The wog says, "That's not a pig, that's a duck." "I wasn't talking to you," the bloke says, "I was talking to the duck".'

Everyone had heard them before, often in the dining hut where muted jokes and grunts would come from Rex's corner whenever the West Indian ate his meal. The man ignored him, although he was always aware of Rex and was just waiting for a chance to catch him across the head with a shovel.

The labourer took his wheelbarrow off for another load. Rex picked up another sheet of plywood, scraping off some loose concrete with his hammer and started to straighten the old nails in it and to bang them back out.

'That lot,' he mumbled, 'should never be allowed to vote. They'd never be able to vote in Jamaica or India. They're alright in their place, but their place ain't here, taking our jobs and wearing their rag hats in them heathen temples. I ain't got time for none of 'em. I ain't seen one of 'em with a day's work in him. Their wives can. The women are good workers. I worked with a darkie once. If he lifted a finger, I'm a Scotsman, heaven forbid. I get sick of all the poufters and ethnic minorities. Life seems to revolve around them nowadays. It's one law for them and one for us. Why should they wear turbans on motorbikes? Oh no, *we* have to wear helmets, but not them.'

He passed the sheet to Seamus and picked up another one. Above them on the pillars that had just been done, the steel fitters had finished the steel frame for the beam and were moving on to the next one.

'We need some more S.G.B.s,' Rex said.

'There's plenty. They're taking off the box in the corner, so we can use those.'

'I'll get a few.'

'O.K.'

Rex went over to the side and chatted for a while with Mick and Geordie. Five stories down, he could see the pedestrians in the street. He wolf-whistled at a woman in a tight yellow dress.

'Can I take some of these?'

'Sure.'

He picked up one of the heavy metal jacks. They were adjustable supports, used to hold the boxes in position at the correct height.

The engineer was nearby with his theodolite, measuring precisely one of the boxes for a pillar, ensuring it was absolutely vertical. Overhead, the crane was lowering a load of steel reinforcement bars onto the top floor and, over on the far side, a gang were puddling down the concrete, levelling the section of the floor off. From somewhere below a transistor was playing, accompanying the brickies as they laid the outside facing walls.

He placed the S.G.B. down and brought over a couple more. Seamus had some wedges and plates. They called over Mick and Geordie to help them get the box into position and place the S.G.B.s underneath it, tightening them until the box was secure.

Seamus then climbed up on top, whilst Rex passed him some wood and ply from below.

'You know, in India, if I didn't obey their laws, I'd be thrown straight down the black hole. So why can't they obey ours, eh? They're going to outnumber us soon. They breed like blinking rabbits. Englishwomen have children, but they have litters.'

He started to make grunting noises like a pig as he passed a piece of ply up to Seamus. As he picked up another piece and started to bang the nails out of it, he started to imitate an Asian trying to speak English, then went on with his diatribe.

'This country will all be black one day. But we can't say we don't like them. The Race Relations Act works against us whites. A publican can't even tell them to get out of his pub. The government should repatriate them all. Give'em the airfare and enough to buy a tin hut over there and they'd be happy.'

What happened next Seamus was not sure, even when he came to make a statement to the police. All he knew was that one moment Rex was babbling away about something and the next he was lying on the floor, unconscious, with a hugh gash across his head. The police found the weapon that had put him into hospital, a shovel, but never discovered who had hit him, or why.

MR SINGH, MR SINGH AND MR SINGH

Mr Karam Singh was walking slowly up the Foleshill Road from the Nanak Sar Gur Sikh Temple. With him were Mr Sarwan Singh and Mr Gurbachan Singh Gill. It was Saturday afternoon and they had just been in the temple to pray and have a good natter about current affairs. Sarwan's son, Satnam, had been there and had read 'India Today' to them. The trouble in the Punjab never seemed to stop. Gandhi was losing control, Karam Singh thought. Congress had done badly in the recent state elections, failing to make any impression in Communist controlled West Bengal and losing Kerala to the leftists. India was breaking up, he thought. Oh, for the good old days.

They had eaten in the temple as well. Upstairs in the old cinema, their community had turned one of the rooms into a large dining area and rolled out long strips of carpet for sitting on to eat. The men had been laying out flowers and carpets in the temple as part of the Akahand Path, which had started on Friday and would go on until Sunday. Thousands of people would come from all over the country to hear Sant Jee and celebrate Puranmashi, the full moon, and thus Guru Nanak's birth in 1469.

It was warm in the June sun. Karam Singh was sweating under his turban. All three were in their sixties. Gurbachan Singh had a walking stick and was quite frail. They stopped every fifty yards or so.

'Come on, old soldier,' Karam Singh teased Gurbachan. 'I thought you fought in Burma, and now you can't walk a few yards.'

Gurbachan Singh smiled. He had served in the 17th Division and had been in the long retreat to Manipur, which had taken a month, fighting on all sides against the Japanese.

'What about you,' he replied. 'You can't crawl on your belly under barbed wire now. Or throw a grenade more than two yards. Hah, better not try, you'd blow yourself up.'

Karam Singh had been a captain in the Indian Army, before he joined two of his brothers in Kenya and enlisted in its army. After that, he had joined the Kenyan railways and worked as a senior controller. Their father's farm in Ludhiana had been over five hundred acres, with a large country house, but on his death it had been divided amongst his six sons and the house was now rented out to the Homeguards. Karam Singh's brother was managing his own and Karam's share together. Sarwan Singh's father had been a carpenter from Nagal Shama village, near Jullundur, where Sarvan had been brought up, until he had come to England in 1950. He had been taken on at Alfred Herbert's machine tools

136

as a material handler, until he had bought his own grocery shop, which he and his wife had run for fifteen years together. Now one of his sons ran it – or rather, his eldest daughter-in-law, who had a much better business head than his son, the day-dreamer. Oh, the arguments over money he'd had with his son!

Gurbachan Singh had been to East Africa as well as Karam, but to Arusha in the Northern Province of Tanganyika, between the Serengeti and Mount Kilimanjaro, in 1946. There, he had been an office manager at a building contractor's for twenty years.

They slowly walked up past Courtaulds and cautiously crossed the road. Karam Singh wanted to look in Joshi Estate Agent's window. He had no intention of buying a house, but wanted to compare the prices of homes similar to his and, hopefully, see how much they had gone up.

'There's one there for £10,950. Oh no, it's not as good as mine,' he said. 'It's only got two bedrooms. It's been modernised though.'

'There's a two-bedroomed one for £12,500,' Sarwan Singh said. 'I think that's the one Gurjit Cheema's selling.'

'Mine's got three bedrooms.'

'I've just had central heating put in,' Gurbachan Singh boasted. 'My son did it. He's a very good tradesman. Very reasonable.'

'So you keep telling us, Gurbachan, so you keep telling us. Ah, a large, three bedroomed house in Leamington Spa. Forty-six thousand!'

'They pay for the area there.'

'Got gas central heating. But still, mine must be worth nearly that.'

'Foleshill's not Leamington, Karam.'

'Here's a detached house in Bedworth. Six bedrooms, two bathrooms, two kitchens, central heating, large gardens. £75,000!'

'That's more like yours, eh, Karam,' Sarwan Singh pulled his leg. 'A bit smaller perhaps.'

'Prices are terrible in this country. Everything is so expensive. It's so dear to get repairs and my sons have no time. They keep saying they will repair the roof, but they never do. And the prices are going up all the time. The young have no time for us today. They are too busy with their colour televisions and videos,' Karam complained.

'Ah, Karam, I must go into Dean's video shop and get Mani Balwaan for Harjinder,' Sarwan said. 'Come on, Gurbachan, we must cross over again.'

The eldest of the three smiled. The traffic had virtually stopped as police cordoned off the road. For the last half hour, the street had been filling up with people lining the pavement, many of them children with balloons and icecreams. In the distance they could hear a marching band. They all hobbled across the road.

Gurbachan Singh had three daughters, two of whom were now in England, one in Coventry, with whom he was now living. She was a bright girl, with a family of her own and worked as a Community Liaison Officer in one of the city's comprehensive schools. He had sent her to Baghdad and Kuwait for her education, to a French convent, then to a boarding convent in India. She could speak French and Arabic and Hindi, as well as English and Punjabi.

They walked past several more Asian shops, one run by a Gujarati. "Sikhs are enterprising," thought Karam Singh, "but not like the Gujaratis. They'd sell their own mothers, if you let them."

Asian parents put a lot of pressure on their children to do well, but they had to. Life was hard, especially in a foreign country and they wanted their children to have what they hadn't. They had come over for their children and now their children were rejecting them.

'It hurts,' Karam said.

'What hurts?'

'Our children turning their backs on us.'

'Yes,' said Gurbachan. 'it hurts more than this arthritis. It makes me feel ten years older. Sometimes I just want to die.'

'I want to die in the Punjab.'

'We never will though. We'll never see it again.'

The band was nearing.. The crowds on the pavement were thickening. Cheers could be heard. The three old men turned, looked down the road and watched as some lorries came out of Broad Street and drove up towards them. It was the head of the Foleshill Carnival. They watched the procession approach, with its floats and children in fancy dress, carrying ribbons, flags and balloons.

'Come on, Gurbachan,' Karam Singh chided.

'I must go into the Bazaar for some karella,' said Sarwan. The three walked past St Paul's Church and into the newly built large supermarket, through the tricky turnstile and into the far corner where the fresh vegetables were kept. The karella was 65p a pound.

'It has gone up again,' Sarwan observed.

'I never know prices,' Gurbachan added. He loathed shopping. It was women's work and he would never demean himself. But his two friends had no such old-fashioned ideas.

'I think I shall get some okra and ginger for Baljit to use,' said Karam Singh, remembering the instructions he had been given when he had left home that morning.

'Chilli is 25p a quarter,' Sarwan Singh noted.

'Mooli is 90p a pound. That's expensive.'

'You sound like two old women,' Gurbachan chastised them. 'Come on. I want my video. If they haven't got it, I'll blame you.'

The other two selected their produce, had them weighed and priced and then walked towards the checkout, but not before Sarwan had made a diversion for some Achar Pachranga pickle and a packet of popadoms with chilli and garlic. Gurbachan was champing his teeth whilst Karam and Sarwan debated whether to get some green lentils or pink peanuts. Then he noticed the drinks' shelves and quietly hobbled over there and chose a small bottle of whiskey, for medicinal purposes.

They met up at the checkout and then left the store to make their way up to the video shop. Outside in the blazing sun, the carnival was passing by, in its noise, gaiety and vibrancy. Brightly-coloured floats decked with flowers, tin-foil, children's paintings and people dressed as animals, sportsmen, or in traditional English and Asian costumes went slowly by. Sounds of disco music came from one, that of Banghara dancing from another, competing with the several marching bands and the cheers and shouts from the crowds and people in the procession.

The three pottered into the video shop. Karam Singh stopped off just inside the door to look at the likes of "Hot Stuff", "Hard Up" and "Young Lady Chatterley", expressing surprise and disgust, after a thorough examination. Sarwan Singh's eye was caught by the video nasties, whilst Gurbachan Singh tottered over to the counter to ask for the Dinesh Ghandi producton of Pranlal Mehta's Mani Balwaan.

The young man searched but couldn't find a copy.

'Sorry, it's out.'

'When will it be back?'

'I can't say. Tomorrow perhaps.'

'Can you keep it for me?'

'It's very difficult.'

'It's for my daughter.'

'I will see. Leave your phone number. I shall ring you if it comes in.'

'I have no phone.'

'I'm sorry then.'

'Wait. My neighbour has a phone. I'll give you his number.'

The young man wrote out a note, with the phone number and the three elderly gentlemen left the shop. The procession had gone past by now, the tail turning off the Foleshill Road, on its tour of the area. The crowds were dispersing, many to go up to Edgewick Park, where a fair was on. There might be a Kabaddi match as well. Karam was looking forward to that. But he was getting tired in the heat and having been on his feet for so long. They passed the sari shops, the Kansara Gift Shop, the Everest Sweet Centre across the road, up to the crossroads at the top of the hill. They crossed the road and entered the Standard Restaurant run by an Asian family and sat at one of the cramped tables.

Karam Singh went to the counter and ordered for them. Three teas, a selection of badam and chocolate barfi and some jalebees. He sat down as they were brought over for them.

It was a good café, offering a relaxed view of life at the crossroads. Opposite them was, on one corner, the Friends Corner Indian and Pakistani Restaurant and, on the other, the "General Wolfe" public house.

They sat and talked. Karam Singh had worked for seventeen years in the Art Gallery. There was resentment in him for that. He was an educated man, who had had an important administrative job in Kenya, one of whose daughters was an M.A. and the other a PhD., yet he had never got promotion at the gallery. He had spent his years as an unskilled attendant and when he had objected to this colour prejudice, he had been demoted to a caretaker for his impertinence.

He felt his hip. There was arthritis in it and he was due for an operation. It hurt when he over-used it.

Gurbachan Singh had come to England in 1968 and joined his brother in Leeds. He hadn't been able to get a job, so had moved to Bradford, where he had been employed as a quality controller in a textile factory. He had stayed in lodgings until he had bought a house, when he was able to bring his family over. Many of his relatives were in England, all over it, in virtually every town. It was such a large family.

They watched all the young people laughing and messing about in the street.

'It's so hard for the young,' Gurbachan said. 'For us, we can go back, and so can our children, but our grandchildren, they don't know India. For them, this is their home, yet they are foreigners in it.'

'The young have no respect anymore,' Sarwan interrupted.

'They can't get jobs. They have no money, they get bored and do silly things.'

'They need more discipline,' replied Karam. 'They need military training. They are so troublesome. The teachers are no good either these days. They do nothing and their speech is terrible. They should teach them more sports to give them more discipline.'

'In India,' Gurbachan observed, 'the schools are always very well disciplined.'

'All the morals have gone in this country,' Karam added.

'The girls get pregnant before they marry. Girls shouldn't go out with a lot of men. The mothers should talk to them. It's all very bad.'

'Their dresses get shorter and shorter,' said Karam, having researched it.

'My wife has always covered her body,' Gurbachan revealed. 'Even after intercourse.'

'The young see no point in education either these days,' Karam went on. 'They don't see how important good speaking and qualifications are.'

Gurbachan Singh sipped at his tea. He was nearing the end of his days and he knew it. Some things made him bitter, if he thought too much about them. He hardly ever went to the temple now, or to a restaurant. His friends called less often and he felt he was losing contact with his family as a whole. He couldn't read and his hearing was going. It was all so frustrating, growing old, not being able to do things. And it was so lonely as well.

'My wife must have a new sari for Harjeet's wedding,' said Karam. 'Oh, the expense! But she must have it.'

'Is Harjeet happy with him?' Sarwan inquired.

'She's very pleased. He likes discos and is clean shaven, so she thinks he's wonderful. That's all they think about now.'

'Arrangements are breaking down these days. We never had so many divorces and break-ups in India. The young are so selfish.' Gurbachan Singh wiped his beard with his hand.

'I think it's good that the young are given more say over their partners,' said Sarwan Singh. This was almost a heresy to the other two, but they were used to him. He was from a lower caste, strictly speaking, though most of those distinctions had disappeared. But he had been in the Indian Workers' Association for many years and supported the C.P.I. when in India. It was the C.P.I.'s betrayal of the struggles in Talengana in '49 and over the Battlement Levy Tax in '59 and of the Naxalites in the late sixties which had disenchanted him. But he still had a picture of Stalin in his front room. He was against a Khalistan because it would lead to a division of the Punjab and more bloodshed, as when Pakistan was formed after the War. On that they all agreed. This Khalistan thing had blown out of all proportion. In their day, Sikhs and Hindus had lived peacefully together. The Khalistanis were always bickering amongst themselves anyway.

The afternoon was passing. They could hear the marching band again in the distance. Their teas and barfi were finished, but they still sat there, talking.

'There are too many poor in this country,' Sarwan said. 'The rich are so rich, they don't know where to use it, but look out there, there are some who can't afford a cup of tea.'

'England is so rich, there should be enough for everyone,' added Karam. 'It's fields are so full of grain, there shouldn't be any hunger.'

'What is happening to morality?' asked Gurbachan. 'We get all this crime because those who don't have, want it. Everyone wants to sleep well and eat well.'

'Some,' added Sarwan, 'have got many houses, others haven't a roof over their heads. Labour should build cheap houses. There are people sleeping on the pavements. The big companies are crushing the workers for more profits.'

The other two did not agree, but kept quiet. In their old age, they didn't

141

want big arguments. They wanted people who agreed with them. Grumble *with* each other, not against each other.

They watched as the carnival came past again, proceeding along Station Street East and turning down the Foleshill Road, with all its joviality and energy. Then they rose and rambled off down the hill towards the park and the festival stalls.

Mazail Singh, Ayub Bhayat and Aman Singh –
taxi drivers

MAQSOOD

School had been hard, as usual, for Maqsood. All his teachers were English and they made so many assumptions about him. They tried to understand, but they never could. The history lesson had been about Elizabethan costumes and architecture, geography and been about the chalk Downs of Sussex and Kent and Urdu had been tucked into the lunch break. He felt it wasn't fair to have to learn it whilst the other kids were playing football, relaxing in the sixth form lounge or, as usually happened, sticking their noses against the windows and shouting "You Paki bastards" and "Paki language" at them.

They were so ignorant, those whites. He wasn't even from Pakistan. His family were Gujurati Moslems, whose home was hundreds of miles from Pakistan. Anyway, he'd never been to India and had been born in Coventry, just like them. It also annoyed him that Urdu was not a recognised part of the curriculum, although the school had a very high Asian population at it. The course wasn't laid down properly and the teacher was left to his own devices. Mr Khan was always complaining that he had no teaching aids or support, and had to make everything himself.

He walked through the flats in Hillfields, towards Stoney Stanton Road, where his family had an old terraced house, past the old stamping works and along Hartlepool Road, taking a short-cut down an entry.

A group of white lads from his school were messing about, pushing and shoving each other. As Maqsood hurried by, one pushed him, saying 'Oh, sorry,' in a joking way, then blocked his path, repeating 'Oh sorry. Sorry. Oh, sorry The others started to laugh. One came up from behind and grabbed his workfiles, scattering his papers over the ground. Some of his Urdu lessons were there.

'Oh look, filthy Paki writing.'

'I didn't know they could write in Paki land.'

'Scribble, more like.'

'Paki scribble, ha.'

'Can't you write proper, like us, then? English too good for you?'

'Don't touch them. You'll get Paki disease. Diarrhoea, or smallpox. They never wash.'

One of them started scrunching his shoes over his notes. Maqsood was pinned against the wall by the other three. He said nothing, letting them get on with it. That way he might not get beaten up.

One of them started ripping up his files and treading his notes into a puddle.

'Now they're dirty, just like you, mud-face.'

'Why don't you leave us alone?' Maqsood said bitterly, but quietly.

'Oh, it speaks.'

'I haven't done anything to you.'

'My dad's unemployed because of you lot. F . . . off back to wog land, Paki.'

'Many of my family's unemployed too.'

'Scrounging off the dole.'

'No . . .'

'Shut it, Paki bastard,' and a fist smashed into Maqsood's mouth. He bent over, clutching his nose. He was kneed in the stomach and, falling to the ground, kicked. One of them jumped on his leg, nearly breaking it.

They were only stopped when two other Moslems came along the entry and saw what was happening. The odds suddenly not to their liking, the whites ran off.

'Maqsood, you alright? Maqsood? The bastards. We'll get them. Maqsood? Oh, your face.'

'It's not too bad,' Maqsood mumbled. 'My leg hurts. That's the worst. But look at all my notes.'

'Your nose is bleeding. Here. Here's a tissue. Hold your head back. Don't get up. Lean back.'

'My jacket's ripped. What's my dad going to say, Salim?'

'He'll understand.'

'He'll say I provoked them.'

'No he won't. We'll get you tidied up first. Come to my house.'

'I'll miss Jama'at.'

'No you won't. There's fifteen minutes before 'Asr. Come on.'

'O.K.' Maqsood rose slowly and Salim helped him walk. The other lad, Abbas, had retrieved his notes and files and, shaking the water off, tidied them together.

'I didn't stand a chance.'

'We'll get them,' Abbas said. 'We'll put out a description to the others. We'll get them.'

They walked to Salim's house nearby. Abbas went off to change.

144

Salim's mother fussed Maqsood and cleaned up his face whilst Salim
wiped the mud from Maqsood's jacket and shoes.

'I've got to change for 'Asr.' Maqsood said. 'Thank you, but I have to
go.' He put on his jacket and collected his things.

'I'll see you after 'Asr,' said Salim. 'I'll walk you up.' Salim had
already changed for the mosque and they walked up Stoney Stanton
Road to Maqsood's house.

'See you, Maqsood.'

'Khuda Hafiz.'

'Khuda Hafiz.'

Maqsood entered his house and hurried upstairs, before his mother
saw him. He washed his bottom and changed into his spotless mosque
clothes. Salim went to the main mosque, as he was a Pakistani Moslem,
whilst Maqsood went to the Gujurati one. The differences between the
two communities were minimal, about some tiny disputes over praying
and the service, but the powers in the Moslem community had seen fit to
split over it, to such an extent that who controlled the Moslem
Community Centre across the road from Maqsood's house was a major
issue.

He looked at his face in the mirror and dabbed off a few remaining
spots of blood from his nostrils. He then dashed downstairs and into the
road and ran along to the Gujurati mosque. It was two houses knocked
together and converted into large rooms.

Salim's mosque was a large, beautiful, purpose-built one, in white,
with a glittering golden dome, arabesque arches and inside, a large,
carpeted hall.

Maqsood went around to the back, in through the gate, past the special
toilets for washing and into the cramped wash room. He slipped off his
loose shoes, put them on the racks with the others, then sat on the bench
by one of the taps. He was barefoot. There were three other men washing
as well. No women were allowed into the prayer room.

He began his wudu by washing his hands up to his wrists, especially
between his fingers, three times, then washed his mouth and used a
brush stick to do his teeth three times as well, then washed his nostrils
and sneezed the water out, three times, then the tip of his nose, then his
face. Next, he did his arms up to the elbows, then wiped his wet hands
over his hair and neck, cleaned his ears with his index fingers, washed
his right foot, then left, all three times. This he had to do before each
Jama'at each day – at Fajr, dawn, at Zuhr, about midday, at 'Asr in the

afternoon, at Maghrib, sunset, and Isha in the evening. Isha was a longer prayer, especially during Ramadan. The times of the prayers changed as the days lengthened and shortened. Ramadan, the month of fasting was when nothing could be eaten from an hour and a half before sunrise to five minutes after sunset. Based, as it was, on the Islamic calendar, it was twelve days earlier every year. This was the year 1407 and Ramadan would fall in May. The year 1408 would start in August, 1987.

Maqsood put his topi over his hair and walked hurriedly through the madrasasa. It was full of boys and girls, sitting at low benches studying the Islamic holy books. An Imam was teaching them. It was quiet, the only sound being the muted recitations each was doing. He went upstairs and into the prayer room. The Imam there had already started. The large room was packed with about forty men standing in lines, their heads bowed in prayer.

There was no talking, just praying. All the heads were covered and lowered. The Imam was reciting at the front, facing east towards Mecca. He knelt down and everyone did likewise, their noses and foreheads touching the carpet, palms of their hands flat either side of their faces. Maqsood prayed fervently, his faith in Allah flooding back in this refound solidarity.

The Imam rose, put his hands up, his thumbs just under his ears, and said: 'Allahu Akbar' then recited the next rakat as the lines of worshippers stood, heads lowered. They all sank to their knees again, bent right forward twice, then stood, reciting 'Allahu-Akbar' again. They all did this for each prayer. At Isah every evening, there were seventeen rakat and, during Ramadan, thirty-seven. The Imam then read a lesson from the Quran and from his own heart, whilst everyone knelt silently. Maqsood prostrated himself several times more, for those rakat he had missed. Then a final prayer was said and it was all over. The men rose, most to leave, but about fifteen sat around the walls to read quietly from the holy books or talk.

The room was the whole top floor of a terraced house, with the walls knocked through. A small door led to the adjacent house, where there was a similar prayer room. The floor was completely carpeted with loose carpets. There were no religious icons or paraphernalia on the walls, no pictures, just two plaques in Arabic saying: "There is no God other than the one God," and "Mohammed is the messenger of God," and a board with the times of the Jama'ats for that day.

Maqsood decided to stay for a while and talk privately with God about the attack on him and how he should react. It was not like him. Yes, he was religious and obeyed the five pillars of Islam, but he wasn't like Salim. He was studying to become an Imam and was far more devout in his whole way of life than Maqsood could ever be. As a Moslem, he believed in God and the prophet Mohammed. He prayed to God five times a day, even if his lessons meant he took Zuhr early, during dinner time. But that was common for Moslems. When his father had worked at the Jag, he had had to fit Zuhr and 'Asr in as best he could. The factory didn't care about his beliefs, so long as they didn't interfere with production. But it did nothing to accommodate them at all. In fact, the racism there had been sickening and his father had come home sometimes with tears in his eyes. Maqsood also strictly fasted during Ramadan and his family gave the zakat, two and a half per cent of their earnings, for the poor and he would be going on his first Hajj to the Ka'bah at Mecca when he was eighteen. His family was largely vegetarian but would eat Halal meat occasionally. The animal had to have its throat cut with a very sharp knife, in one stroke, whilst the name of God was recited. All life belonged to God and it was not for men to take it, thus every animal had to be offered to Him, so it would ascend to Heaven. Despite criticism that it was cruel, he believed it was painless to the animal. It let the blood flow out rapidly and that was healthier. Meat with blood in disgusted him. Nor did he drink alcohol. It led to fighting and unreligious behaviour.

Maqsood thought about the boys who had attacked him. They probably believed in God and Jesus Christ. They attacked him for being different, yet Christ had taught the brotherhood of man. He couldn't understand it. Moslems were far more tolerant. Christ was one of the prophets of Islam, but he was not the son of God. He did think Christ was alive and would return one day. He also believed in Adam and Eve, the Flood and in Noah's Ark. Abraham himself had built the Ka'bah and the Bible was one of the four written books of Islam, though Moslems called it the Injil. The other three were the Taurat of Moses, the Zaboor of the prophet Dahood, father of Yusef, and the Quran.

Christianity was so intolerant. It belived it was completely right and no one else was. Their God was the only God. He was white and male and had all the values of the English middle class. In fact, Maqsood knew, Christ was black, but they'd never admit it. Islam, though, believed all religions served the one God and it accepted their prophets as the prophets of Islam. There were 124,000 prophets altogether, Adam being the first and Mohammed the last. All the universe was under the control of God, who had created it all in seven days. Allah was a power. He had no face nor form, and it was forbidden to represent him in paintings, or the face of Mohammed.

He rose to leave and said goodbye to the others, including his uncle sitting in the far corner. He went downstairs, through the madrasasa and into the back, where he put on his shoes, took off his topi, and walked home, back past the community centre.

It was an old church they had converted into a hall and an advice room. The Hindus had been after it, but the previous owners had not wanted alcohol drunk in it, so had given it to the Moslems. The advice centre helped with filling in forms, translating, passport enquiries and problems with government departments, usually housing and D.H.S.S. It was a place for the elderly to gather and talk, with some food provided as well, and held karate and Urdu classes on Sundays. It had cost over fifty thousand pounds, which had all been raised from individual donations. His father worked there voluntarily a few days each week, since he'd been made redundant by the Jag. He had come to Coventry in 1960 and his first job had been at Alfred Herbert's Machine Tools, as an unskilled quality inspector. He had returned to India in 1964, for three years, then worked at the G.E.C. in Stoke as a machine operator, until he'd moved over to the Jag in 1971. He had also helped get the funds for their present, makeshift mosque and was involved with raising the £300,000 for a new one to be built. The sacrifices of their community were enormous. There were over ninety mosques in Britain. The one in Glasgow alone had cost three million to build.

He went straight upstairs to change. His mosque clothes must be spotless and used for nothing else. If a dog were to brush against them, he would have to wash them again. It was such cleanliness which made jokes about "dirty Pakis" so stupid, ignorant and ridiculous.

He went down to the kitchen where his mother had prepared the evening meal and kissed her. She didn't notice his face. They had to wait for his father to return from visiting his sister in Foleshill before they could eat the vegetable dahl, japatis and salad, but he stole a piece of barfi to see what it tasted like. He remembered Salim and decided to go and visit him at his study centre.

The Jamia Islamia was barely thirty yards away. He turned through the yard door and into the alleyway beside it, then into the school. He took off his shoes and quietly went into the large, carpeted study room.

148

Salim was sitting at one of the old school desks arranged into a large square, quietly reciting from the Quran. He looked up and waved at Maqsood before returing to the book. Maqsood sat down to wait.

The room had been the front of a shop once and the old shelves were still fitted to the walls. Carpets lay on the floor and there were a number of books at the side. The chairs, as well, were old junior school ones and were slightly too small for comfort.

This was the study centre of the Pakistani Moslems, many of whom were from the Kashmir. To Maqsood, it was all the same, but his father wouldn't be pleased if he heard that Maqsood had been here. The Imam rose and picked up another large, old book and took it back to his desk. He kissed it before opening it. Three students sat around him and he began to read from it, explaining the passages whilst they took notes.

Salim was in white. He had a youthful beard growing in black tufts on his chin and a lace woven topi on his head. It was made in five parts, to signify the spiritual leader. He wore a humble white top, white trousers and shoes with the heels trodden down to form slippers.

To become an Imam, Salim would have to complete seven years of study. The youngest students often started from eight years old, attending after school, but next year when he became sixteen, Salim would be at the study centre all day. Here, he read the Quran, learnt to read, speak and write Urdu and Arabic and read the other holy books. Arabic, the language of the Quran, was taught in seven different subjects: sarf (grammar), nahv, Islamic sharia, the hadis of the Holy Prophet and the explanation and translation of the Quran.

As he sat there, several teachers came in, followed by Mr Siddiqui. He was an important man in the Moslem world. He walked over and shook Maqsood's hand, then those of all the students, greeting them in the name of Allah and the Prophet. He had agreed to speak to them and sat at one of the desks to deliver his thoughts. Mr Siddiqui had been Imam of the Holy Data Darbar Mosque and Shrine in Lahore. It was amongst the greatest religious shrines in Pakistan, where all the political leaders had come to pray and ask for his support, especially during elections. But he had stayed out of politics. He had toured the world, giving lectures as Vice President of the World Islamic Mission and President of the International Moslem Organisation. He was also President of the Moslem Scholars of Britain and Chairman of the Trust of Jamia Islamia.

Mr Siddiqui had a presence. The Indians call it karma. It was a calm authority. He was dressed completely in white, with a greying beard. He was a large man, with eyes that won immediate respect. As Maqsood sat quietly in a chair at the far end to him, he was filled with awe.

He spoke firstly about the children. About how they no longer respected their elders and were more and more abusing God. But, he said, the children learnt from their parents, and it was they who must be good Moslems first of all. They should spend their lives according to the Islamic law.

Islam was a way of life, with moral laws from the cradle to the grave. The Holy Prophet gave them many hadis about business, neighbourliness, politics and relationships. The Quran taught how to solve every problem and it was the duty of every Moslem to consult it. If the answer wasn't there, he must turn to the hadis and the Moslem scholars and only then to his own thoughts and decisions, so long as he acted within the rules of Islam.

The elders were turning away from the Quran. The pressures of Western society were great and they weren't always praying five times a day. Fathers were swearing at their wives in front of the children, they were abusing them, drinking alcohol and even separating. Such things only destroyed the future happiness of their children.

Maqsood, like Salim, Mr Siddiqui and most Coventry Moslems, was a Sunni. Unlike the Shi'ites, they had no heirarchy, no titles and no Ayatollahs. The only position was that of Imam. The Shi'ites believed that Hazrat Ali should have been the first Khalifa of the Holy Prophet, whereas Sunnis believe that his selection as the fourth Khalifa was right and proper and he had no precedence over the other three. The split in Coventry was between two groups of Sunnis and had arisen about fifteen years ago, about the time Maqsood had been born (though he always denied that it was his fault!). The Gujurati moslems were mainly the followers of Mohammed Bin Abdul Wahhab, who wrote a book many hundreds of years ago about the prophet. So they believed in some different ways of the Prophet and in some different laws. Then there were the differences over the way one should hold one's hands whilst praying and over the size of the new mosque when it was built. Maqsood also suspected that the split was over personalities and along community lines as well. There were still disputes even now over control of the new mosque.

All religious differences, Mr Siddiqui said, were created by men, not God. Islam alone had seventy-three different sects, all with minor disagreements, but that paled beside the thousands of Christian groups. Men refused to get together because of pride and ignorance, but they all should join one another and work for one purpose.

The meeting was finished with a prayer. Maqsood and Salim left the gathering in the name of Allah, put their shoes on and went out. The Jamia was also a cultural centre. The money for it had been raised from the Islamic community. Public meetings were held there every week, discussing how to be a good Moslem under the conditions of a society which affected a Moslem's life like a bad engine effected the smooth running of a car.

They usually discussed how to save their religious values. They would welcome people from all religions and Mr Siddiqui had participated in joint services at Coventry Cathedral, as part of the effort to spread harmony, understanding and peace in the world. But, if Maqsood's father knew he'd been there, boy, would there be trouble!

MR KARTAR SINGH & MRS PRITAM KAUR*

We then went to the flat. Standing outside on the ground floor, I could see that the kitchen window had been smashed and not yet securely boarded up. There were muddy shoeprints on the front door, where someone had succeeded in kicking it so hard that the wood on the inside, into which the lock fitted, had been broken. The door had "N.F." signs on it. On knocking the door, Mr Singh shouted 'Hang on!' several times whilst his wife had to get down on her knees to unbolt it.

The sight of Mr and Mrs Singh left me stunned and horrified. Mrs Kaur was bent double. Her head, whilst walking, was virtually at hip level and she lead her husband, who was almost totally blind, by the hand into the living area. She asked her husband to switch on the light, as she was afraid that, if she drew back the curtains she would again attract the white tenants, who would taunt them at the window, or throw something through it. Mr Singh spoke fluent English, but Mrs Kaur did not speak it at all.

I explained to the couple why I had come and Mrs Kaur was thrilled when she heard. She said they had been made to live in fear of their lives for the past ten years. She said they had never had a proper night's sleep, as someone was always kicking their doors, or shouting at them. She also complained that there were no Asian shops in sight and it was very difficult constantly relying upon English food shops.

Mrs Kaur said she was at her wits' end now and wanted to move out straight away. Mr Singh, however, was very disillusioned and kept repeating that there was no-one anywhere who could possibly help them and that there was no hope for him. Having explained why I had come, Mr Singh said he was only prepared to move if his son gave him the O.K.

Before we actually discussed alternative accomodation, Mrs Kaur said that her husband had been refusing to sign the pension books for a long time and she was finding it impossible to manage without money coming in. She produced a plastic bag containing three pension books, dating back eighteen months to September 1984. No money had been withdrawn since that date.

I asked Mrs Kaur how she had been managing and she stated that she had been relying on her son there to give her what he could. She then went on to say that at one point, she went through a whole month with nothing more than water in the flat. I asked Mr Singh why he had been refusing to sign the books. He was very stubborn in his replies and I decided to be firmer with him. He then agreed to sign in thirteen places, for the past three months.

* This story is based on an actual social worker's report. The couples' names have been changed.

MRS BANTI KAUR*

Mrs Kaur was sixty-two when we found her. She had lived with her son and daughter-in-law and their family for eight years. She was living in one room at the top of the stairs, where she was kept all the time. She was never allowed down and visitors were never told about her. Food was left for her on the stairs.

She was physically abused by her son and tormented by her daughter-in-law, who encouraged her children to call her names and to not respect her.

She was entitled to a pension of £37.50 a week, but her son used to put a cross on the slips and cash them himself. He told her she recieved only four pounds and that they were entitled to that for her food and bills. She stayed with her son for another three months after we had spoken to her, but then he evicted her with no clothes or furniture.

Social Services reassessed her needs and housed her in a Part Two scheme, in an independent flat, with a warden and alarm system. But it was an all-white scheme. She had no furniture and was sleeping on the floor. Other tenants said she suffered from screaming fits and woke up early in the morning to have baths. When we spoke to Mrs Kaur about it, it was evident she didn't know how to use the electric cooker and had burnt her hands on it. Not knowing the alarm procedure, and not speaking or reading English, she had run screaming with pain into the corridor asking for help, shouting 'Meri mudat karo!', 'Help me! Help me!' the other tenants had slammed their doors in her face, making her more distressed. Eventually, the warden had helped her.

Special provision needs to be made for Mrs Kaur. There are linguistic, cultural and social factors which make putting a single Asian person in a sheltered residential unit unsatisfactory. She is far from Asian shops and the temples. She cannot speak English nor read notices. She cannot watch the T.V. and there is no video machine provided for her to watch Asian films. She has withdrawn into her room and feels cut off. The other residents now see her as aloof and unfriendly.

It is the Asian tradition to wash early in the morning and to use a bucket rather than a bath, which requires a tiled bathroom. Other residents have complained about the smell from her cooking, but she has the right to cook, like everyone else. There is only one cooker provided and one set of pans, whereas she is a vegetarian and needs vegetarian-only utensils. There had been no one available to explain to her about the electric cooker, which she had never used before.

She has suffered from hidden, prejudiced attitudes, especially amongst agencies. They have often required her to speak English. They have complained that she won't fit in, yet refuse to provide for her special needs. They often simply refer her to the Asian agencies, thus pushing her and their responsibilities away. Everyone pays lip-service to racial equality, but they all expect black faces to fit in with white culture. They refuse to adjust, or to accept that the Asian elderly have a different life style. Agencies have made a lot of petty requests concerning Mrs Kaur. Can she not wash so early in the morning? Can she make sure there are no smells? Can she stop pressing the alarm? Mrs Kaur has been put under tremendous pressure to change, but, being elderly, it is extremely hard for her to and she feels very frustrated and isolated. She feels she cannot use the communal areas and the other residents make no effort to socialise. She does not understand white games, such as bingo, quizzes or dances. She can't read, even her own language, yet no one comes in to talk to her or read her the paper. There is no recognition of her religious days, of Diwali or Vaisakhi.

There is a strong argument to rehouse Mrs Kaur in an all-Asian residential scheme. Adequate provision can be made for cooking and washing. The design of the rooms can allow for prayer areas and for the different design of Indian homes, with fewer internal doors and more archways. Wallpaper and decoration can reflect her Sikh culture. She could have a small garden plot to grow rare or expensive herbs, such as thania and poodna, and flowers for worship. Also, the average height of the Asian elderly is less than for white people, so the cupboards and surfaces could be made lower and she could have more cupboard space for her spices.

There is a strong tendency to class all Asians as the same and a failure to understand the separate cultures of the Sikhs, Hindus and Moslems. In training, whole religions are described in a paragraph. There is also a belief that the Asian elderly are looked after by their families. This is not so true now. In England, housing is for the nuclear family and so many households are overcrowded and have no room for the elderly. Many feel that they have paid their taxes and rates for many years, so their elderly are just as entitled to care as the white elderly. The respect for the elderly is breaking down. They are no longer accepted as the heads of households and, because they are not contributing financially, are resented and left to fend for themselves. Many are isolated, with no family support and get very depressed. Many young Asian families are also finding it hard to find work and cannot afford to feed any more mouths. Also, many elderly themselves want to remain independent. They don't want the noise, overcrowding and disruption of a family, but want peace and quiet. They often don't want to move with the family to another city, where they will have no friends. They cannot cope with the westernised ways of their children.

Also, much white privately rented accomodation is inadequately heated, damp, cramped and insanitary, with very poor furnishings. Some Asian elderly don't realise they can claim for their rent to be paid, so pay it out of their pensions. There is no welfare system in India, so they start from the belief that they are entitled to nothing. They are very ignorant of their rights. The fact that Asian youth is becoming westernised is a big ego-boost for white society, but ignores the fact that Asian elderly value their culture and want to hold on to it. They are seen as uneducated and backward, whilst the youth are civilised and westernised, but are still repressed by the elderly, through arranged marriages, and so on. This is not the case, but a white, middle-class prejudice. The so-called limitless freedom of the West causes isolation and depression. Many Asian youth, having tasted "freedom", want to return to their old values and ways, when faced with the illusions and harsh realities of society.

The case of Mrs Kaur highlights many of these problems. Discussions are now being held with Church Housing and the Council to find her better accomodation and see that many of her difficulties are solved for her.

* This story is based on an actual social worker's report. The woman's name has been changed.

Broomfield Road, Earlsdon

155

TONI, HARJINDER AND SHAMSHAD

Toni rose to order the teas. Like Harjinder, she was a teenager whose parents were Sikhs. She herself wasn't sure she believed in their religion anymore. She felt there was one God, but He was not the preserve of any one religion. Sikhism meant far less to her than it did to them.

She returned with the teas. Shamshad was a Moslem from the Gujarat in India. She was untypical, her family being very lenient towards her. But for her, as well as the other two, there was a distinct line between her family and her social life.

'Those pesty boys are in here again.'

'Oh, ignore them.'

'If we can.'

'I bet they start something soon.'

'They always do.'

'Preetiben was in a state yesterday.'

'Why?'

'Her dad told her, if she didn't pass her "A" levels, they would marry her off. They've got someone for her already.'

'My parents are like that.'

'It's emotional blackmail.'

'We have to live with it though, don't we.'

'No, they're also doing it for our own good. If we got a good education, we could marry who we wanted to. They only want the best for us. Most of our parents say they only came over here for our sakes.'

'I'll just make sure I pass, that's all.'

Both Toni and Harjinder came from landowning families of Jats, traditionally the highest caste, who looked down on the Sahani, the lowest caste, of pot-makers and even on the Takhan, the carpenters or businessmen. In Coventry, despite in theory having no casts the Sikhs had seven temples, one for the Jats, one for Ram Charhia, a group of the carpenters, and so on.

'Mother had another letter from India,' Toni said. 'They want to send their cousin to us over here. That'll be the the fifth. It's too much.'

'Girls?'

'Yea. They send them over for my mum to find them husbands. They stay in our house for a few months, until she finds them a husband, then we never hear from them again. They disrupt our family and it costs mum a fortune.'

'I know. Arranged marriages are so expensive.'

'The last one cost four thousand pounds.'

'Is your mother head of the family?'

'Oh, yea. They write to her, asking her views on all sorts of things.'

'How can she decide, being so far away?'

'I dunno. But that's the way they do it. Our family's huge.'

They were all nineteen and studying at the Butts Technical College, doing "A" levels. Harjinder and Shamshad were doing Social Science, whilst Toni was attempting Chemistry. Sometimes, they came up to this little café in the dinner hour, just to get away from the college. Many of the lads hung around the restaurant all day, drinking coffee. It was somewhere to go, something to do. A lot of them saw no real point in exams anyway. Unemployment hit them far worse.

'I want to get out of Coventry,' said Harjinder.

'Why?'

'I can't stand it. It's a hole.'

'Where'd you go?'

'London Poly. It's more exciting down there. Nothing ever happens here.'

'What'd your parents say?'

'Oh, they ain't that strict. So long as they knew I was alright. I'd stay with relatives. I hate it here. Everyone knows you. They all know your business.'

'I know,' said Toni. 'It's terrible. If someone sees me with a boy, my mum knows about it even before I've got home.'

'It's not fair. The boys can get away with anything. But if we're seen with a group of boys, even if it's only walking down the road, it's all nudge, nudge, wink, wink. They all see who you're with and what you're doing and then they tell your parents.'

'I might as well forget an arranged marriage,' laughed Harjinder. 'I don't stand a chance.' 'I'm boy mad, I am. Even in the temple. I'm terrible. When mum takes me in, I know all the boys there. She notices that.'

'They notice everything. Watch out, Toni, they'll marry you to a turban wearer, just to keep you quiet.'

'Oh, no.'

'Why?' asked Shamshad. 'What's wrong with a turban?'

'Oh, no, he'll be so old fashioned.'

'What chance does he have, if even Sikh women don't want him?'

'But it looks horrible as well.'

'He might be very nice.'

'Yea, but it's too traditional. I want someone with modern ideas.'

'Like what?'

'Well, who'll treat me like an equal, you know. I won't live like my mum did.'

'I think there's a lot of good in tradition,' insisted Shamshad. 'I wish I'd learnt more about Islam and my culture.'

'My parents made me learn Punjabi, but I refused,' Toni revealed. 'Then, when I was fourteen, I decided I wanted to learn, but after three lessons, the teacher threw me out. He said I was completely useless. He refused to teach me.'

'I don't want to lose contact with my family. It's a hard world and I think I'll need them to go back to.'

'I don't. I think it's so suffocating.'

'I hate everything to do with India.'

'I hate everything in this country. I want to go back one day.'

'I don't. England is my home.'

'It'll never be mine. I can't stand all the prejudice.'

The Asian lads on the space invader machines were laughing loudly. One of them knew Toni and came over, but, in front of his mates, he was cocky and too aggressive. They chatted, but he didn't stop long, as he was called back, away from "girl talk". Instead, they occasionally hurled some pointed comment as they were ignored.

'I feel like two different people,' Shamshad said. 'I'm one at home and one at college.'

'I don't like having to lie to my parents,' said Toni.

'But they're so out of date.'

'What annoys me,' Harjinder said, keeping an eye on the lads, 'is boys can get away with anything. If I say anything at home, everyone ignores it, but if my brother opens his mouth, it's a big event, to be recorded for ever. If he said "I want to be a policeman," the whole family would discuss it for months.'

'I can't stand the temple either. All it is is a dating agency.'

'Our parents haven't adapted. In India, there's nowhere for boys and girls to meet, so they need arranged marriages and they work very well.

There are hardly any divorces. Two people aren't just thrown together, their families consider for ages if they're suited.'

'Yea. That's changed. I don't think my parents would force me into a marriage I didn't want.'

'Young people believe in love and romance, which soon goes.' Shamshad said 'Our parents see things much more sensibly.'

'I don't agree. That was O.K. when boys and girls never knew anyone else to compare, but now we do. I think if you don't know anyone else, you do find it easy to live with someone all your life. But I know lots of boys. I know I wouldn't be happy with just anyone.' She stared over as the boys fought playfully over whose turn it was next.

'I won't ever promise my parents to bring my children up as Sikhs. It's up to them if they want to believe.'

'It's too late then. If you don't bring them up in your culture, they'll lose it forever. I think you have to bring them up as believers, if you're to really give them the choice.'

'How do I know what *I* want, let alone my kids?' asked Toni. 'I've never seen the need to learn Punjabi. We all speak English. I can speak Punjabi a bit, but it's like slang. My mum can't understand it when I speak. I don't care. When I get really heated, it's a total mixture of Punjabi and English.'

The lads were pulling faces at them, making Toni laugh. Shamshad wanted another tea, so slid out from the table to get her round in. On the walls were pictures of Cyprus and Greek religious postcards. Above one table was a copper engraving of the Parthenon. The father who owned the shop had a well-tanned skin and was heating some sausages in the microwave whilst his daughter, lighter skinned, was serving the teas. The café was full, mainly of factory workers from across the road on their lunch-break. Shamshad returned with the teas.

'The great extended family. You can stuff it. All it ever does is gossip, gossip, gossip. I don't get any support from it. They just stop me doing what I want. I hadn't any say in where I went to college.'

'They fear losing us, that's why. It's their biggest fear. They want to keep us close.'

'It's claustrophobic.'

'They don't want us to have any freedom.'

'We're all they've got. Without us, they've got nothing. Look how proud they all are in their children.'

'Yea. They push us into education, to get degrees, just so's they can

159

show us off. "Look, my daughter's got a degree. The other one's a doctor. We gave them freedom, but they used it well."'

'I think we owe it to them.'

'We're losing our identity. We're neither English nor Indian.'

'I'm not. I'm English.'

'No, you're not. We're not accepted here. We're still outcasts. White people will never accept us.'

'I don't know what my identity is,' Toni said, looking down at her cup.

The café was starting to empty as the factory workers left. The owner and his wife were sitting at a table, both having a cigarette. The Asian lads were picking up their bags to leave.

'Going back to college?' Toni asked.

'No way. We've got a football match up Edgewick park.'

'Got no lessons?' inquired Harjinder.

'Manjit has, but he's coming anyway.'

'What'll your parents say?'

'I don't care.'

'We'll have to tell them you know,' Toni teased. 'You're not doing your duty as a son.'

'Stuff that,' Manjit replied. 'I work enough. There's no end to it.'

'What's the point anyway?'

And with that, the lads set off for the park.

'There's always got to be a barrier between people. Look at the Golden Temple. When Ghandi sent the troops in, all the Hindus were cheering. It was the holiest Sikh shrine, covered with blood.'

'But when they assassinated Gandhi it was worse, wasn't it. I was in Southall then and all the Sikhs were holding parties and celebrating and dancing. It was more a festival!'

'But, Shamshad, the Sikhs always believe the Hindus repress them. That's why so many want a Khalistan.'

'Do you?'

'Our parents do.'

'Mine do,' added Harjinder.

'They wear the orange turbans of Khalistan.'

'There was a march outside my school. The Sikhs are much worse than the Hindus.'

'We've got more grievances. Girls were being raped in the Golden Temple. That angered me, so I could understand how angry they were in India. Bhindaranwala was an idiot, but now he's a martyr.'

160

'Racism's stupid though. Remember that car crash, when two Moslem boys died, but the two Sikhs and two Hindus were all right? All the Moslems wanted to know why only the Moslems died. They wanted to get their own back. All those gangs went round.'

'The Moslems had the Black Fist.'

'Stupid.'

'It's any excuse for a fight.'

'It's like that in every culture, though. Like the skinheads and mods.'

'Yea, but when Satnam Singh Gill was killed, we all stuck together then.'

'And Opinder Pall. He was stabbed at a party and thrown out into the road. The whole community got together then. The police got them. Just as well. '

There was a pause in the conversation. Toni was distracted by the zapping of invaders from Jupiter or somewhere even more exotic. Some schoolboys were buying Lion Bars and cans of Lilt from the counter. A postman with his empty sack came in for a batch. One of the boys grabbed one of his mates' sportsbag and ran off with it, followed by a string of expletives and inanities.

'White people always tell us to speak in English when we're together. One said to me, "When you want to claim dole, you lot want to be English, but otherwise, you want to be Indian." But he only wanted us to be English when he wants. I feel torn both ways all the time.'

'Someone's always upset. Either we're too English, or not enough. Either they want us to integrate, or they reject us.'

'I think our parents have compromised a lot. My mum lets me wear makeup and I can cut my own hair,' Shamshad explained. 'They're more concerned that I keep believing in God and keep praying.'

'Some won't compromise. They still make their children wear suits.'

'But then they change on the way to college.'

'It's so maddening. They look so innocent and their parents don't know a thing about it.'

'I saw two girls go upstairs into the toilets in British Home Stores, all dolled up. When they came out, they'd changed, no makeup, all nice, innocent girls.'

'Then we all get a bad name. My mum says "Look at those lovely girls, with plaits and no makeup. Why can't you be nice like them?" and I know they go down town and get changed.'

161

'Once, just to spite them, I went to London for two weeks and worked in a MacDonalds. I stayed with my uncle, but I didn't tell them.'

'I couldn't do that. I love them all,' said Toni. 'Even my brothers. On Rakhee, I always buy rakhri for their wrists.'

'You just want their money.'

'I got a job in a restaurant, but they wouldn't put me on the till for ages. I was kept hidden in the back. They always took the mickey out of my accent and made me pork batches.'

'We can't object though, can we.'

'No chance. I'd've been sacked on the spot. Then I got 'Paki' all the time. It got to me.'

'One employer actually told me he didn't think I'd be good for his company. He didn't care that I had the best qualifications, or if I'd work hard, or anything.'

'I'd appeal. Not because I'd get my job back, but just to let them know we know our rights.'

'My mum doesn't know hers. They won't allow a union. She works in a sweat shop off the back of Foleshill Road. Steaming trousers. There's a little room downstairs, with all the windows closed and barred up, with about ten steam irons in it. The place stinks and gets hot and sweaty. Ugh. She can't read English either.'

'The unions are as racist as the management.'

'I think they work together in some places to keep black people out. So as not to rock the boat.'

'My mum doesn't even know she can take goods back to the shops and get her money back,' said Harjinder.

'The receptionist at my parents' doctor's is a racist. Once, when my mum had gone in to see the doctor, she said, "They take advantage, don't they." She didn't see me, but I told her that was my mum.'

'I can't trust my Indian doctor. He's the family doctor. He's very good and likes to talk, but I wouldn't trust him.'

'Not all our parents are the same. I think we stereotype them,' Shamshad told the other two.

'I don't trust any of them,' said Harjinder.

'They've got my life all planned out for me,' Shamshad replied. 'When I'm going to be married, which college I'm to go to, where they want me to live, even my daily routine.'

'Girls seem to be nothing. We're just got ready for marriage. They can't wait to get rid of us.'

'When a girl's born, it's like a funeral. When my sister Nina was born, everyone told my father how sorry they were. He cursed her. Mum cried at her birth. She was only two hours old and they were already wondering how they'd get her married off.'

'My mum takes every bit of gossip to heart.'

'Mine couldn't care less. She just hopes I prove them all wrong.'

'I'd never put up with what they have. Mum has to worry about the relations in India all the time. They're like parasites. She did everything for them, but they went and sold off her land in India and if she doesn't buy their relations enough things when they get married, they throw it back in her face. "Oh, she didn't buy me a choora at my marriage." They're looking for a passport to get here. I'm never going to marry anyone from India.'

'It gives us some power over them, though,' Toni laughed. 'If they do something we don't like, we can threaten to divorce them and they'll have to go back.'

'Or they'll take a dive, to avoid being found,' Harjinder added.

'My cousin was married recently,' Toni said. 'The poor couple hardly got the chance to meet. The daughter's family came to the matchmaker's house first, then the son's. The families talked for ages, to see if they liked the daughter and my cousin. They'd already been through months of negotiations before this. The matchmaker is responsible for the marriage. If it fails, it's his fault, so he had to make sure they were suited. Then, when the families decided they liked each other, the matchmaker asked the couple if they wanted to talk. They were taken into the kitchen by my uncle, who sat with them and told them "No touching, just talking." My aunt had to go in and drag him out, so's they could talk properly, but he was back in five minutes to see if he'd attacked her or raped her. The girl gave my cousin a list of questions her father had written down for her to ask him, like his career, money, where they'd live, you know. He said all they wanted to do was talk about music and where they liked to go out.'

'Is he happy?'

'Oh yea, he's very pleased. The matchmaker did a good job. They were very suited.'

'It's like a contract between the two families.'

'Yea. They agree on the dowry, right down to the last item. She had to give my cousin a house, T.V., video, sofa, all the carpets and one double and three single beds.'

'Cars are given sometimes.'

'It depends on how rich the family is.'

'Moslems don't take the dowry so seriously. It isn't even mentioned. With us, the boy's family approaches the girl's, after they see her at weddings or if they've heard about her. But we let the couple alone for hours in the house. We don't have a matchmaker.'

'It's so expensive to marry a daughter off though, isn't it. At the wedding, her family has to buy all the suits and gold for my cousin's family. We always marry in the girl's house as well.'

'One thing I don't like about Islam,' Harjinder said, 'is men can marry more than one wife. I don't think that's fair. I think women should be treated as equals.'

'But we're more independent now,' said Shamshad.

'Yea, I think it's all breaking down.'

'A lot of Moslem girls are going away to college or university.'

'I think our parents are accepting it more. There's far less conflict.'

'Yes,' Harjinder nodded, getting ready to go. 'My younger sisters get away with murder now.'

LADY HERBERT'S GARDENS

At the top end of Lady Herbert's Gardens are some seats set into secluded alcoves. Often, they are the innocuous haunts of alcoholics, peacefully passing out the days, usually leaving a liberal collection of lager cans and wine bottles behind them, in the waste baskets and under the seats.

On this occasion, under the wisteria hanging down and hidden by the cherry blossom and lilac, an Asian lad and girl are kissing and laughing. She had to go up to Manchester soon for an arranged marriage to someone she had never met. His parents, like hers, would be furious if they found out about their secret rendezvous. So the two steal a few last minutes together before they succumb to their parents wishes.

Bill Luckett, independent dairyman

THE AUCTION ROOM

The auction room was a low-hanging hall, jam-packed with household bric-a-brac. I was there to buy some carpet for my stairs. I was late and the auctioneer, a stocky man in an expensive leather jacket and chain smoking, was already on lot seventy. He rattled through them.

'Lot seventy-one. Washing machine. Hoover, is it?'

'Servis, John,' replied the porter.

'Servis washing machine. What's it like?'

'Pretty good, John. Start at a tenner.'

'Right. Let's start at a tenner then.' There were no bidders amongst the sceptical and sharp-witted crowd.

'Come on, a tenner for it. It's nearly new. We can't guarantee it, of course, it's bought as seen, but it looks pretty good to me. A fiver then. Come on, let's get on. No one interested at a fiver? I'm not letting it go for less. It's worth at least that.'

A reluctant hand went up.

'I've got a fiver.'

Another hand.

'Six.'

The first comes back. At head nod all that was required now.

'Seven.'

'Eight.'

'Nine.' Then the second bidder shakes his head. 'Going for nine. All finished?' He scans the crowd, then sharply bangs the top of his biro down on the lectern to signify the sale. No gavels here. No unnecessary equipment or noise. Even his lectern was makeshift, as he stood on a table, with his papers resting on the top of an old cupboard.

Most of the crowd, about fifty people, were not well off. There were a few in suits, perhaps businessmen on the lookout for office equipment. There were a lot of private landlords, many Asian, hoping to furnish the expensive bedsits and houses they let to students with shoddy furniture. The sight of these landlords, squabbling for a few quid over a tacky secondhand bed or chair made me sick. One week's rent would have covered the entire contents of a room.There were some students there as well. Only a few, looking for bikes or beds or some item they needed.

I pardoned my way through the people packed in the narrow main aisle which ran between the lines of old goods radiating from it. I walked down each side aisle in turn, picking my way carefully in the cramped space, bending down to look under tables or reaching up to inspect a piece of carpet slung on top of a wardrobe. Each article had a sticky label on it with a lot number. Lot seventy-two was a broken stereo. It went for three quid. Seventy-three was a box of crockery for seven pounds. The incongruity of the bidding was interesting. It didn't matter how much something was worth in the shops, but how many people wanted it and how badly. Crockery was easy to sell in the many secondhand shops in the town. A broken stereo wasn't worth the effort, unless you were in that line of business. Quite a few of the bidders were owners of these secondhand shops, regular customers at the auction. Some were known for regularly taking any books that were available, others for household linen, others for cookers and fridges. These dealers would chat amongst themselves during the sales, no doubt agreeing not to bid against each other, further cutting their margins in this sale of tack and trash.

'Where there's muck, there's brass,' I murmured to the bloke next to me. I had seen a piece of carpet, lot a hundred and thirty-two, and was thinking of getting a cup of tea and a hot-dog at the little tea counter before it came up.

There were two rooms. This, with the really cheap stuff, and another where the better stuff was sold. In that room, over a hundred people crammed in to bid for bedroom suites, dining tables, fridge-freezers, good stereos, and the like. Some of the items there were new, perhaps slightly factory soiled, or, what was quite common, being sold because of a shop or office bankruptcy. So some weeks, if a business had closed, filing cabinets, electric typewriters, swivel chairs, desks, everything, would be there and businessmen, dogs living off the dead remains of their competitors, would compete for the rich kill, salivating at the cheapness of it all.

Or a hotel may have shut down, releasing beds, carpets, wardrobes, chairs, catering equipment and much besides into the auction and the other landlords would gather round, Shylocks, figuratively rubbing their hands, yet, even in such morbid circumstances, still quibbling over a couple of pounds for a virtually new colour T.V. going at a quarter of its shop price.

Lot ninety-four was an old chest-of-drawers.

'Nice chest, that,' I mumbled.

'Yes,' the man next to me said, 'it was me dad's.'

'Oh,' I said, embarrassed.

It went for three pounds fifty.

'That was his as well,' he said, indicating the next lot, a cupboard. 'All his stuff's here. There was nothing we could really use. Just junk.'

I was surprised at his attitude, although he was plainly upset. It went for seven.

'The funeral was a week last Sunday. They came round and offered fifty quid the lot. I didn't feel like haggling. They could have taken it for nothing, if they'd wanted. It makes me sick, seeing everything he had go for next to nothing. What are we?' he asked. 'What are we? We work all our lives and, when it comes to it, everything we ever had is knocked down for fifty quid.'

I wasn't in the mood for his father's life story, so I excused myself and pushed through towards the tea counter. There was a small queue. Nearby, behind a glass screen, three young women were going through the sale dockets which recorded the buyers of each lot and the prices. A man was arranging transport to bring his purchases to his shop and reading off a list of the lots he had bought. It was long.

I bought a tea and a sausage and tomato batch. It was very cheap, a welcome relief from the general money-orientated atmosphere. Observing the bidding, it seemed that quite a few people were there just to watch. They were friends, family, business partners, or simple curious people off the street. Only about five or six were regular bidders, going through a list of lots, all with the maximum price they'd pay beside them.

My lot was coming up fast as the auctioneer, between mugs of tea and cigarettes, skated through them. He obviously found it a bore and a chore to flog through these remnants of life, himself frequently expressing frustration at items going so cheaply. He wanted to start the bidding for a double bed at ten pounds, someone offered only five and he decided, nuts to them, it was worth a tenner and he wasn't going lower. It eventually went for eighteen. Sometimes though, such things wouldn't find a buyer at all.

The aim, of the auctioneer was to sell every lot: to clear the salesroom. Space meant money and if a lot wasn't sold, it meant another lot couldn't go in next week. Quite a few weren't sold. Even at fifty pence or a pound, if no-one wanted one double-glazed window or an old high chair, then there it would stay. Hanging from the beams running overhead, there

168

were large hooks, carrying kids' BMX bikes and other, more valuable items. Those bikes tended to go for quite a sum, up to thirty or forty pounds, if in good condition.

My lot came up. I had been getting more and more tense as it approached, anxious not to miss it and wondering how high I'd have to go. It was a nice roll of brown carpet and I'd decided on up to twenty, thinking it would cost me nearer eighty in the shops. I had squeezed nearer to the auctioneer and when he started at five, wised up, I offered three. I was ready to nod again. He asked for four. Again he asked. No takers, so he banged down his pen, asked my name and went on to lot one-three-three. I was amazed. Somehow, I'd imagined that something I valued, others would also value and I'd have to face stiff bidding. But no. It was towards the end of the sale, many people were leaving and I'd got it for next to nothing. I noticed the man again.

'Not your dad's carpet?'

'Nah. You've got a bargain there. I'd best be off. I can't stand it.'

Looking around, I decided to leave as well. I went to the office and arranged the delivery of the carpet, then headed for town, as the final lots were being auctioned off.

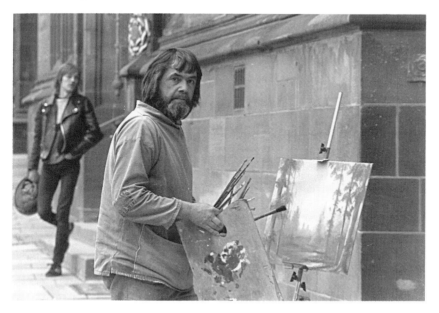

David Hale, painter

169

THE S.A.S. POSTMAN

Little did his colleagues know that, when Alan came into work that morning at ten past five, he was a changed man. Not a woman in his life. No, he had finally snapped. Saturday had been the final straw, the dog that broke the postman's back.

He had been bitten so many times in his career that his bottom was riddled with as many craters as the moon. His legs had so many scars he looked as though he'd been hit by a shrapnel mine in the last war. He deserved the Distinguished Service Medal for some of the paths he'd been up.

So, over the weekend, he had planned, assembling all his equipment and hiding it around his body, under his uniform.

He strutted in, making strange rattling noises and went up the lift to the sorting floor and signed in. There, the night shift had already done the inward primary sorting of his mail, separating it from the other rounds, but he still had to set the letters in his frame into the individual house numbers.

There were over twelve hundred delivery officers in the Coventry and Warwickshire district. His was a patch of Eastern Green, a suburban area on the way out towards Birmingham. Suburban, but highly dangerous. As he set the letters into their slots, he recalled every branch of every tree set just at head height, every overhanging flower basket with his blood on, every gate with an impossible latch or a catch which nipped his fingers, and every letterbox fitted with a draught excluder which refused to admit any letters at all. And especially every variety of vicious, rabid hound lurking behind a doorway or garden hedge.

He set some of the never-ending "junk-mail", occasionally termed "Rebate" or direct mailing. Then the piles of holiday offers, catalogues, bank mail and mail-order offers, leaving some for the second post, which tended to be lighter.

He went over to collect his "packet bag", a large sack which contained any small parcels he could deliver, then carried it back to his frame.

During the evening and night, the mail had arrived from the station and been emptied into concertina bags, all numbered and the weight checked for the work-load assessment of the amount of mail being handled. They were then set into rows in large trays, those not postcoded put into coffins to be hand-sorted. Meanwhile, the parcels were sorted for the van drivers to set them out, put them into skips and wheel them to the lifts and down to their vans.

"'Struth," he thought, "do these catalogues never end?" He had visions of being lost under a huge pile of them, his dried bones discovered years later.

"What's it today?" He glanced at it. "Only go straight in the bin. Ooops, can't say that, can I. Our biggest customer."

Those personalised letters or catalogues from firms were the bane of his life. And there was so much financial mail these days – bank statements, building society books, credit cards. He reckoned nearly half of his mail was financial now.

It was Thursday, so he had a few giros to set out. There were only a handful. After all, it was suburbia, not a large council estate where most of them were unemployed and where postmen were waited for with desperation and greeted with abuse and grunts of 'Why're ya late?' He did have one though, a Mr Wilkinson, with a tongue like a sword.

But today was going to be different. Today, the worm had finally turned and he would take no more. He dreamt of a huge bonfire with all the world's rebate mail on it, a huge pile stretching right up into the sky, and he had the match to set it alight. Up so early every morning, in bed by ten at night, only one day off a week, no social life, all to be abused and attacked. It was too much, just too much.

The P.E.D. came round, checking and supervising. Alan grunted. He didn't properly wake until half-six. Any attempt at civility before then was impossible.

There was a letter to be redirected. He checked the change of address on the green redirection card, then resorted it by sticking a yellow label on and ticking the "Gone Away" box. He then wrote his duty number and the date and filed it. Another house had a small parcel, so he marked a "P" on a letter for the same house, to remind himself. He walked around to the security cage to collect his registered mail, signing the tab for it and then walked back.

"Wrestling on tonight at Bedworth Civic Hall. Great. I wish they'd put me in there with some of those dogs though, then we'd see some fun."

There were a couple of letters with no house numbers on and he didn't recognise the name, so he pulled them out, filled in a couple of yellow slips and dropped them into the dead letter box. Next, three recorded delivery letters had to be noted into a note-book, with the date and address. He wrote an "R" on a letter immediate before each one.

With all the letters set, he now pulled them out and bundled them in the sequence he had found was the quickest and easiest, binding each with an elastic band and numbering it. He had just finished this when someone came along with some missorts from the other rounds. They were a blinking nuisance. He had to open the bundles up again, flick through the letters and insert the new mail. More time wasted, and his round was miles away, right at the bus terminal.

'You got a screw missing, Alan?' the bloke next to him asked.

'No, why?'

'You're rattling like an old tin of nails. And I could've sworn I saw steam coming out of your ears.'

'Ha, blooming ha.'

He started bagging up the bundles. The worst time for missorts was Christmas. Kids would just write, "Auntie Flo, Coventry" on the envelope. They thought postmen were mind-readers.

The letters filled three sacks. One had an address and time written on it. That one would be dropped off on his round by a delivery van, left in a safe place.

He took a couple of the little white cards called "form-lefts", to be filled in if a person wasn't in to receive a parcel. Then he slung the other two heavy sacks over his shoulders and made off, past the coffins with letters and parcels still to be sorted, downstairs and out into the cold, brisk January air before stroding off towards the bus-stop.

Approaching it, he saw his bus pulling up at the stop. He ran as best he could and was just behind when it pulled out. He shouted, screamed and banged the end of the bus, but the driver was in an equally bad mood and, frankly, couldn't give a fig. The bus left Alan cursing amidst its diesel fumes.

There was a ten minute wait before the next one. He boarded it and sat down, getting angrier and angrier. "All this," he thought, "six days a week, for a hundred and twenty quid top line."

Fifteen minutes later he disembarked and made for the flats where he hid one of his sacks, whilst he delivered the other. It was still dark.

Now was the time to put his plan into operation. He checked the time on his watch, took out a tin of shoe polish and blackened his face, pulled a black balaclava over his head and took off his jacket, to reveal a rope and hook, some small wire-cutters and a number of other tools he thought might come in handy.

172

Six years he'd been on a round in Allesley, with hardly a bite or an incident. He'd loved it and the people had been really friendly. But two months here and he had taken all he was going to. He slipped out the back with his sack, ran quickly across Hockley Lane and into Morgans Road, nipping silently down paths, through hedges and over fences, getting nearer and nearer to the first of the sneaky hounds.

Those dogs were cunning. They had an alarm clock in their heads which automatically went off whenever a postman was within a hundred yards. They would lie in wait until the legs walked up the path or the fingers opened the letterbox, then, all savagery was let loose.

Alan neared the house where an alsatian was kept in the back garden, and where the letterbox was in the back door, of all stupid places. You'd've thought some people never wanted letters, the trouble they went to to hide their letterboxes. He quietly slipped the letters into their boxes as he approached the house. A few doors away, he nipped down an entry and came to the garden from the back. He peered over the fence in the gloom. There was the alsatian, alert behind the high gate, quietly waiting, wagging its tail in anticipation of a bit of lively amusement chasing the postman up the nearest tree.

Alan slipped through the back gate. He had a football rattle in one hand and one of those attack alarms in the other. He quietly made his way across the lawn, breathed in, then charged at the dog, screaming, letting the alarm off and swinging the rattle around his head. The dog faced him in blind panic and shot off, across the lawn and out of the open gate, with Alan in hot pursuit, his sack bouncing up and down on his back as he did his tribal war dance.

Curtains started to open, doors were pulled ajar, and heads came out to see what was going on, but by then the blackened shape had slipped back into the bushes and all was quiet again.

He waited a few minutes, then nipped back out and finished posting letters along the cul-de-sac. A couple of people were on their way to work, but neither noticed the silhouette behind the hedge.

He legged it right up Hockley Lane, posting as he went, then had a stretch of dead walking to the next drop-off in Manderley Close. He had to work a loop down it and back up again. A second dog lurked a little way along, a small terrier, hiding in a porch, and it received the same treatment as the first. The porch door was flung open and suddenly a mad, shrieking, rattling, screaming, dancing ogre in black scared the living daylights out of the petrified pooch. Then more curtains drew back, a woman rushed to the porch to pick up the paralysed, cowering animal and wondered what on earth had happened, for Alan had disappeared as mysteriously as he had come. She picked up the letter on the floor and went back inside.

On the determined man pressed, back down Hockley Lane, emptying a postbox on the way, back to Garrick Close for his second sack, then off again, round the back of the flats, avoiding the few people and setting off in the pre-dawn shadowiness.

A mongrel met a similar fate as it waited for him behind one of the hall doors, but again, no sign of the culprit as he slipped rapidly away.

Mr Wilkinson would be waiting by now, standing at his gate, cursing. Alan scooted out, lugging the heavy sack, shoving the catalogues and rebate mail in the addresses as he went along. He was running late, what with all the diversions, angry because if he returned late the canteen would be full of all the office staff ordering long lists for all their workmates and he'd be waiting ages for his eggs, bacon and black pudding.

He burned along, up and down the drives in Sutton Avenue. At one house, he noticed the milk and mail hadn't been taken in for a couple of days, so he promised to knock on the door on his second round, to check they were alright. "Oh," he thought, "to get promoted to Postman, Higher Grade, off delivery and onto the keyboards tapping out the postcodes. That has to be easier."

There was a first-day-cover letter, which he handled carefully, anxious not to crumple it and pushed through a letterbox. He could see Mr Wilkinson now, so started scaling fences and hedges, rather than let him see him coming down the road.

He was his own boss on the round, that was what he liked about the job. The fresh air didn't particularly appeal. To be honest, it was a nuisance most days. He wasn't a born walker either. It was the fact that there wasn't someone there all the time, telling him what to do. And there was the pride he felt in doing a good public service well. It was the best postal service in the world, he reckoned. Pity there wasn't a bit more pay, though. Trouble was, there wasn't much overtime, just an occasional delivery to cover for someone off sick. On nights they got more. He had tried that once, but it had so mucked up his body system that he had gone back on delivery. It didn't matter so much to him, he wasn't married, but for those who were, and there were as many women who worked for the post office as there were men, the hours could upset your family life.

He didn't get any time to think about how pleasant a day was, or to look at the scenery. He had to concentrate on the job and make sure he wasn't mis-delivering.

He squeezed between a hedge and a wall and jumped over a flowerbed, crouching low now. For three months he had been on a two week rotation with another delivery officer, sharing two rounds, but then that bloke had decided to do just the one. They only had single duties now, though.

He banged his head on a hanging flowerbasket as he stood to look for Mr Wilkinson, then went over another fence. The man was only a few gardens away now, half hidden by a cypress tree. Over five hundred drops, there were, on his round, yet last Christmas he had only five tips and Mr Wilkinson had still screamed at him and hurled as much abuse as he did every two weeks on benefit day. On his old round he had been given forty-seven pounds once. He hadn't been offered a single cup of tea on his round, either, though Mr Wilkinson had shaken a full cup at him once, spilling most of it in the process. They kept themselves to themselves round here.

He took out the rope and quietly swung it round and round, then hurled the hook up over a tree branch. Mr Wilkinson was up by his gate, watching the pavement and his watch, cursing the time. Alan swung over the fence and dived behind a hydrangea bush, flicked the hook off the branch and slipped round the side of the house to the letterbox, posted the giro, then quickly stole down the drive into the back garden, watching in case his wife was at the kitchen window, then nipped out the back gate. He hurried back up the back entry, returning to the top of the street, then re-emerged onto the road. He had quickly wiped off the boot polish, taken off the balaclava and put on his jacket again. He mimicked going up and down a few drives, just for effect, then drew up to Mr Wilkinson.

'Where's it then?'

'Where's what?' Alan asked, walking past the gate.

'You know what. My giro.'

'Not seen it, Mr Wilkinson.'

'I bet you've hidden it, or had it yourself.'

'Now, Mr Wilkinson, that isn't fair. I'm sure, if I'd've had it, I would have delivered it by now.'

'Where is it then?'

'As a matter of fact, I've heard a rumour that the Social have checked on you and stopped your benefit.'

'What d'ya mean, stopped it? They never have? I'll see to them.'

'It's only a rumour, mind.' Alan was enjoying his revenge.

'What'm I going to do?'

'They said they'd noticed you standing at your gate, waiting for your giro, so you couldn't be properly look for work.'

'But I am, I go down the Job Centre three times a week.'

'Well, that's what they said.'

'Heavens.'

'I think they're watching now.'

Mr Wilkinson looked around.

'I noticed a suspicious van just up there,' Alan pointed up the road, with his thumb over his shoulder.

'Oh, heck, I'd better get in. Thanks for telling me. I won't be standing out here again.' And he ran back towards his house. By the time he found his giro, Alan was well gone, off round the corner, hurrying through his last drops, before catching a bus as it was just leaving the terminus, looking forward to his breakfast with more than usual pleasure.

THE BUZZ

The yellow and black double-decker bus came to a halt outside Tile Hill community centre. Within half an hour, the mobile nursery was full of three and four-year olds. The driver, Alan, chatted to one as she sat in a chair at the front, pretending to drive it. Three more were doing string paintings downstairs whilst beyond the safety gate, up the stairwell decorated with kiddies' paintings, another half a dozen were either having a story read to them, constructing a wooden Brio railway, or were making dinner in the wendy house. Everywhere, the bright yellow Buzz had paintings and childrens' models, bringing colour and making it into a mobile wonderland, a grotto of hidden delights and new experiences.

THE WHOLEFOOD STALL

'I think education has separated me from a lot of people. That sounds very snobby. But some people never think about their lives. They don't think about what they're doing or what they want. I went to public school. I was a failure, I was no good at it, but it still had an effect.

'I enjoy running the stall. I didn't always. I'm not a health food nut. I don't eat meat anymore, but I used to. It wasn't any moral concern for animals that made me give it up. It was poverty. I couldn't afford it. I was on the dole and I always owed people money. I was always in debt. I lived off soup, cabbage and curry-powder for a year. Literally. Every other week I treated myself to a loaf of bread and some cheese. I love cheese. I could eat a pound a day. It was desperate. Then I knew this bloke who was a herbalist and wanted to set up a practice, but he had to have a wholefood shop as well, so he asked me and Jemma to run it.

'We got onto the Enterprise Allowance Scheme, you know, you get forty quid a week for a year. I didn't know anything about it. But, I thought, it's got to be better than the dole. It made me feel useful. I mean, I like wholefoods, but I wasn't dead keen on them. It's never been my whole life. I think that knowing people who cooked vegetarian food helped. I learned how to cook without meat, so I made a virtue out of necessity. It's still hard. We've still got large debts. We've been at it years now and I'm only just realising how to run it and get it all together.

'There are some real characters who come up to the stall. This little Chinese woman spends ten minutes looking at all our dried fruit and bran, what you have, then thinks of something exotic we haven't got, and says "Why haven't you got any fresh dates?" or something. "Because it's the wrong time of the year," I say, swearing under my breath at her. "Drop In The Ocean have got them." "They've probably got a date palm in the basement, then." Every Saturday she comes and goes through the same process. She hasn't bought anything yet. Then this old man says, "How much's your bran?" "Sixty-four pee a kilo." "I can get it for sixty-three at Drop In The Ocean." "Bully for you," I reply, "Go and eff off there, then." But if we had it for sixty-two, he'd buy the lot. Most people don't even bother to say please or thankyou. But I like the regular characters.

'Drop In The Ocean is the other main health food place. But then they've got a proper shop, so they can stock a lot more. We're cheaper than them, mind you. But some things are so expensive. Dried apricots have rocketed in price. They're ridiculous. You can be too cheap. Then people think they can't be worth buying. If they're expensive, they think they must be better. People are strange. We keep an eye on Drop In The Ocean, sneak in there and compare prices, make sure we're a bit cheaper. Sometimes we even buy things there. You know, if a regular customer has a large order, but we haven't got one or two items, we'll go in there, rather than the customer having to go. It's business sense. Common sense, really.

'Before we had the stall, when we were in the shop, I didn't know anything about wholefoods. But it has become a financial necessity. I can help the customers choose and tell them how to prepare it all. Then they come back again. We have the stall on Fridays and Saturdays only. Jemma and I run it. She's the driver as well, whilst I'm the one who struggles with the accounts. At times, it's pretty quiet. Then I watch people. I study them as they go past. I like to think about what they're like, what makes them tick. People go round so depressed. You know, slouching shoulders, heavy eyes, mouths sullen, not talking, just getting from A to B, as though everything was a chore. Life is a chore for them. Then a woman pulling along a kid, who starts to cry. The mother says, "You're fed up? How do you think I feel?" and whacks him around the head. I can't stand that. Some people seem to enjoy being unhappy. They do. If you suggest anything exciting to them, they act as if they don't want to know. Society's never done much for them, and it shows.

'So why should they care? Some people are happy. They'll go for anything. Others won't. Depression is like a disease. It's an affliction. If you have nothing to look forward to, if you're unemployed, what have you, if you've got nothing to live for, it's not surprising some people just mope around. But they could do something about it. Some don't seem to want to make the effort. There aren't jobs, but you can still do something useful. The thing is, some don't see the point. Unemployment does that. It completely depresses some people, drives them down until they can't or won't pull themselves up again.'

There was a dress shop opposite his stall and a lace and cotton haberdashery, doing only moderate trade as well in the cold January air. Someone came up and bought a tin of Barleycup for ninety-five pence.

'It's one pound twenty-nine in Drop in the Ocean,' he said. 'I don't believe in charging the highest prices I can get away with. I don't believe in exploitation. All selling's exploitation. Even if you say you're earning it by having the stall, manning it and so on, you're still getting people to pay more for it than they ought to. Everything should be free. And I won't have anything to do with ads, or special orders, or posters, or raffles. I hate gimmicks and I can't stand persuading people to buy things they might not want.

'I might be poor, but I've got my principles and I think they're the most important thing. That's why I'm in Greenpeace. I feel strongly about how people treat animals in the world and how they abuse themselves. They're abusing themselves all the time. Eating meat is abusing yourself, as well as the animal. Look what people do to the seals and whales and battery hens. It's the same as men hitting women or mothers hitting their kids.

'Peoples' lives seem so useless. There seems no point to them. They're not doing anything. They're not living, they're just existing from day to day.

'I do believe in development, but of the *individual*, the development of one's own awareness and understanding. I don't mind people who are ignorant about meat eating it, but those who do know about how animals are treated, they've got no excuse. They ought to be vegetarians. I find bloody bits of animals cut up on display disgusting and highly offensive.'

He had on two pairs of trousers, three pairs of socks, fell boots, jacket, scarf and a Greenpeace badge. The stall was laid out very neatly, with the pulses and beans, then the dried fruit, then the Indian curried vegetables, then the oats and bran and, at the back, honey, nuts and finally the Barleycup.

'There's a lot of this world I find impossible to defend. I think a lot about things, especially about how people treat each other and how they treat animals.'

'Are you not of this world?' I asked. 'Are you alienated from all the greed?'

'Well,' he replied, 'you have to live in the world as you find it, when all's said an' done.'

People were busy rushing past, many going in and out of the swing doors of the indoor market, with its jam-packed stalls, its bustle and its life.

'People don't realise their own potential. Power is linked to money. Even just having money changes you, gives you security. It's almost as though people need security before they can enjoy themselves. It's an attitude of mind brought on by the way the state imposes itself on everybody. The invisible "they" has got them exactly where it wants them to be. People must realise and develop their potential, that's what I'm trying to say.'

THE AMALGAMATED ENGINEERING UNION

'The fall in employment has had a dramatic effect upon our union in Coventry. More so than other unions, because we are concentrated in manufacturing, where the collapse has been the greatest. We had 42,000 A.E.U. members in Coventry, but now it's down to 30,000, many of whom are retired members or unemployed. Our due-paying members are somewhere like 20,000 now. And that fall's all been in the last six years.

'Three of our five women staff have left and not been replaced and we have consolidated the two districts into one, losing a full-time official as well. It makes this large building seem empty, with only the four of us in it.

'The new factories opening tend to be smaller as well. They are much harder to organise. The boss is often more paternalistic and says he'll take care of them. It's very hard to get union recognition in places like that. The bigger plants still take notice of the union and consult it. They have to. Production is much more complex these days. The management wants to be able to bargain with one body, not a load of separate individuals. It wants change and a happy workforce which accepts that change. It wants to use the union.

'Although the economic climate mitigates against strikes, there are still a lot going on, often not reported in the press. Union power has *not* been crushed nor diminished. Employers don't want there to be no unions, they want *tame* unions. But now the workers are using the ballots to their own advantage. They look on them as legally binding instructions to strike, when they're not. They've learnt that a vote to strike will often get an employer to up the anti without any action having to be taken. They use the ballots to up the offer.

'The stuffing's been knocked out of this city. It's no longer the Detroit of England. The mood of bouyancy and optimism has deteriorated. People are reluctant to have a night out. There's a lot of pessimism about. There's a growing gap between people in work and out of work. Employers are only recruiting from people already in work, because they're short-sighted and believe the unemployed have lost the work ethic. So the thousand just made unemployed at Massey Ferguson are all being helped to get other jobs by the management up there.

'The most disturbing part for me is to see the apathy of the unemployed and the youth. The moral fabric of the city is under strain.

'It's a period of great social change. Technical change, change in the role of women, with the pill and divorce and families splitting up.

'All our expectations, personal freedoms, expressiveness and education have been raised. But what's the use of all that if you've no money? It makes you *more* bitter, *more* aware of your plight, *more* alienated. Society's polarised now into twenty per cent well-off, twenty per cent in poverty and sixty per cent floating in between.

'Kids these days have a very hard time of it. A lot see no point in education. They're being educated for the dole these days. And there's a terrible background of fear of nuclear war, especially amongst schoolkids.

'We're being alienated from human feelings and perceptions. There's a disconcern for animals and factory farming. Babies are being bought and sold. In some countries, you can sell your kidney, lung or blood for money. Society is being commercialised, with all this advertising, marketing, fashions and raised expectations. It's all very hard for people on low incomes. There's a big gap between T.V. dreams and reality. They manufacture needs to get people to work harder. You've got to change your kitchen every five years now, to stay with it.

'And meanwhile, the government returns to "traditional" methods, to repression, rather than to solving the problem.'

Old Ford's Hospital, Greyfriars Lane

181

Tower blocks and concrete
Are no longer the debate;
Their era is past.
The issue now is nothing
And the decay of what once was.

Hillfields tower block estate

FOUR SNIPPETS

In a house in Edgewick live a man, his wife and their three children. There is no room for grandpa. Behind the house is a coal shed, barely eight feet by six. It has been whitewashed and has a bed, a chair and a potty. Nothing else. It is January and there is no heater. The door is wide open. Grandfather lies on his bed, staring at the ceiling.

*

Walking along Lower Ford Street, past the second-hand furniture shops and houses converted into flats, I pass a family walking the other way. There is mum, her sister, two little daughters and gran, all eating chips.

*

In Wood End, an old man sits in his small flat. He sits on the brick he has sat on all the weeks he has been there. He has no bed, no carpets, no curtains, no cooker, no fridge, no table, no chairs, no lights. He has nothing but the brick on which he is sitting.

He is "discovered" by a member of the tenants' association, who immediately spreads the word. Within a day, people have donated many of the essentials, the rest having come from a garage store run by the tenants' association, and they have put them all in and transformed the place. If it hadn't been for that chance call, he would still be sitting on his brick now.

*

'It was my job to go round in a van, asking people whether they had a T.V. licence.'

'I didn't realise the Post Office did that.'

'Yes. There's a special section for it now. I did it a few years ago. I had a list of every household which didn't have a licence. I had the power to take them to court and prosecute them. I had no right of entry, but often people let me in anyway. Some of the things I saw! I came from a very sheltered background. I never knew there was such poverty. A woman with kids would rather feed them than pay for a licence. I mean, sixty pounds is an awful lot for someone on social security. Sometimes, they wouldn't have any carpets and only really old furniture. I felt awful about that. Then they get fined and have to pay back a pound a week out of their benefit.

'But then, some houses had no carpets, but the biggest T.V. and video machine you ever saw.'

JIM AND THE TELEPHONE BOX

I wanted to phone my parents in Nuneaton, to ask about the weekend. My family were due to go over there for the day. I left our little two bedroomed flat, walked along the dimly-lit corridor, through the swing door with its glass smashed, and waited for the lift.

I soon realised it was broken, so had to descend the eight stories by the stairs. I wasn't too upset, as the lift usually stank of urine anyway.

On the fifth floor, I held the door open for a woman who had struggled up the stairs with a baby and her shopping. The lift was there, its door jammed open by a metal bar. The bar had also been used to gouge out the panel of buttons, which was hanging from the wires. I went on down to the bottom.

Outside, I walked under the scaffolding erected to put the new uPVC windows into all the blocks. At the end, a new lift-shaft was being built. A couple of men were carrying in some insulation boarding and what looked like new wall-heaters. Just as well, I thought, as the walls were like paper and the underfloor heating was so expensive no one could use it. I had to take clothes *off* when I went out.

I walked past the paper blowing around the grounds, and dog excrement, towards the sole telephone box on the estate.

As I approached, I noticed a buggy parked beside it and saw the dark silhouette of someone inside the kiosk. Slowing down my pace, I sauntered nearer. There was glass all over the path and, in the well-worn grass, a mongrel was worrying a plastic bag, violently shaking it in its jaws. I leant against the wall by the telephone box and resigned myself to a wait.

There were in fact, two women inside the kiosk and I soon heard their giggles and laughter. The buggy, as if to match the box, also had two occupants, one a two-year-old and, strapped in on top of him, a six-month-old baby.

I impatiently scuffed my shoes and walked too and fro past the box to ensure the two women knew I was there, that I was waiting and that I was anxious to make my call.

The two year old started to cry. His dummy had fallen on to the path. The crying soon turned to a bawl and I started to panic. Obviously, I should do something, but what?

I went over, picked up the dummy, cleaned it as best I could and hurriedly shoved it back in the gaping, red mouth. Thankfully, bawls turned to cries, then descended to bubbles and finally, muted whines. But baby was not to be outdone. He had discovered a new game. Out came the dummy and it was thrown to the ground. I gave him a stern look, then desperately glanced at the women in the kiosk. They were still laughing away, ignorant of the situation. I picked up the dummy and popped it back in. Out it came again. Plop, onto the path. Again, I picked it up, cleaned it and put it back in. Plop, out again, a broad grin spreading across baby's face.

The two year old had been watching all this, bemused, but he now remembered his mother wasn't there and the cries started again, the dummy not ejected, but hanging in the side of the screaming mouth. Obviously, he was uncomfortable as well, with the baby plonked on top of him. Several minutes had passed by now and still there was no sign of the mothers ending their conversation. Baby, being pushed from below and hearing the screams, forgot his game and started to bubble as well.

"Oh, no," I thought, "not *both* of them." I quickly unstrapped the baby and lifted him up, then started to jig him up and down. I walked back and forth and tried to sign language my plight to the two women inside. They waved and nodded, then went on talking.

A young man passed, pushing a wheelbarrow loaded with leaves and rubbish. He was part of the refurbishment programme, an attempt at window dressing, to tidy up the grass verges, bushes and paths. It was costing a fortune and, though it did employ people from the estate, did nothing to overcome the major problems of loneliness and the general decay of the badly built flats. Most people expected it would all be back to what it was within three months anyway.

Some eighty per cent of the people on the estate were unemployed. Young, single people were being moved in, because families couldn't be expected to cope with life in a block, but it meant that the community was very transitory, with few long-term residents, or people who had developed an identity with the community. In fact, it was destroying the community itself.

The baby was still crying.

I walked up and down, bouncing him on my arm. I tried to find a flower in the verge. I showed him the wonderful graffiti on the wall. I talked about the beautiful scaffolding.

'Look at the pretty block of flats,' I said, trying to sound enthusiastic,

'Look at the doggie.' Doggie immediately started to soil the pavement, which fascinated baby, but then began to bark, which started the cries again. There was also a warm wetness coming through his baby-grow and soaking my shirt.

"Oh, this is ridiculous," I thought. The other one was still crying as well. At last, the kiosk door opened.

For some stupid reason, all the two women could do was laugh, though what was funny about me trying to bounce a screaming baby in one arm, singing to it, whilst I pushed the screamer in the buggy too and fro with the other, I shall never know.

EDDIE AND THE HILLFIELDS
TOWER BLOCK CAMPAIGN

I had known Eddie for several years, off and on. He had recently moved out of his flat in Hillfields House, one of the eight storey blocks in Hillfields, to a ground floor flat in a terraced house owned and recently renovated by the council. He complained of the damp there and it was certainly cold, even with the fire on. I kept my coat on. It was one-bedroomed, with a kitchen, bathroom and living room, fairly spacious, but there were still a lot of things which needed doing to it, touches of paint on doors, the hallway to be finished, and so on.

'I've not worked for four years,' he said, 'I've only done a couple of weeks work in that time. I've been basically ill since then. I've been on invalidity benefit for so long. Once you're on it for some time, six or twelve months, I can't remember now, you qualify for the long-term scale. The long-term scale was originally for people out of work for over a year, but this government, since it came in in seventy-nine, has twisted and distorted the rules, to get every bob out of you in a hundred different ways.

'I moved to Coventry to find work. I heard things were better here than in Scotland. They were for a year or two. Wage scales were higher here then and there were better jobs. It's all Irish and Scots here. Coventry is a very cosmopolitan town. I sometimes wonder what the hell I'm still doing here.

'I was a storeman in Rolls Royce, but I had terrible stomach problems. It's got worse in recent years. It's the Irritable Bowel Syndrome. It's a malfunction of the system. I get sick, stomach cramps, don't go to the

186

toilet when I should do. It's getting worse. I've been waiting until I get better before I look for a job. But I probably won't work again. My body clock's gone to pot. I sleep for twelve hours, but still I get tiredness, headaches and tired eyes.

'I keep myself pretty busy. I read the papers, walk, do the chores, go to the library, you know, everything like that. I like to read history, politics, social science, everything.

'We started up the tower block campaign after people living in the blocks had been complaining for years about the conditions. The blocks had a lot of problems. People used to get respiratory diseases living in the damp. There were some people with mental problems as well. The rubbish shutes would get blocked up with people leaving their rubbish all over the floor. Some blocks had a problem with prostitutes and brothels. There was every problem you could imagine. One thing was housebound mothers. They felt very isolated. Isolation was one of the biggest problems. You'd get depressed up there and the doctor'd give you pills to cope with it. Dogs and kids used to foul the stairs and lifts and passages and some people complained about loan sharks coming round, bothering them for money. It was pretty bad really.

'So we set up an organising committee. I was acting as secretary. We organised meetings for people to complain about the conditions in the flats. But the council didn't want to know, so one bloke took the council to court for damages. We put leaflets around all the doors and invited the local councillors to come and meet the local people, but they wouldn't, until eventually they did, after a load of excuses. We had a meeting with the local councillors. Eighty people were there. It was really successful. We made our point. The councillors were really put in the picture. They had consistently said there was nothing wrong with the flats. But we got photos taken and blown up large and put on boards, of all the damp and filth. We did a questionnaire and everyone told us about their problems, especially the big, drafty windows and the condensation. You see, the flats were very difficult to heat. They were made of that no-fines concrete, which used to let the heat flood out. All the heat went phut – straight out, it just evaporated.

'So we presented all this to the councillors. There were so many problems it was depressing listening to it all. It's inclined to wear you down. Security was another problem. There was an air of delapidation about the place, and neglect. It was so apparent. The councillors were never seen in the area, unless there was an election of course, to drum up votes. After that, they couldn't care less. There was a great turnover of people in the blocks. People wanted to move out as soon as possible. So it was very transient and it was impossible to build a proper tenants' group. People tended to organise around one issue, then it would all die away again.

'It did have an effect. The councillors were really shocked by what they saw. They hadn't believed it. When they saw the state of some of the buildings, even the blind could be made to see, so overwhelming was the evidence. They did seem rather subdued. I think it did have an effect.

'But I claim no victory. We were anti-tower block from the beginning. We were aiming for the complete demolition of the tower blocks and to get people rehoused. There were just so many social problems involved with tower blocks. I think they're anti-social totally. No one ever felt any community spirit at all. They shut people up in little pigeon boxes in the sky and all the doors have three or four chains on them. That sort of thing.

'There was an awful lot of vandalism and burglaries and break-ins. Unemployed people watch people leaving their flats then break in and clear the place. In a conventional street, people watch the street, they keep their eyes open and see what's going on. But in those boxes, you can't see what's going on. There's no security. All sorts of people walk in. The lifts were swimming in urine. Your windows get broken at night. The lifts get vandalised as well. It's terrible for the elderly and women with prams. Up all those flights of stairs.

'They are monstrosities, there's no other word for them. The councillors and architects responsible for them should be placed in them and blown up along with them.

'Yes, we used to get blues going on. Not so much in my block, but in some of the others. They had parties that used to go on all night and all the next day. Drinks were sold there and they were used for business activities. We used to phone the police, but they didn't want to know. They were scared of a riot. "It's not our jurisdiction" they said. The police kept a low profile.

'There was a possibility of riots a few years back. Hillfields isn't Brixton or Toxteth, the West Indian community isn't as big. But we still get incidents, when black youths go through the streets, confronting the police. But the police and council and local paper work together to play it down. "That sort of thing doesn't happen in Coventry," they say. The area isn't policed enough. The young blacks are anti-police, but the old are very glad to see them. You see, there are quite a few muggings around here.

'There isn't so much racialism in Hillfields itself. It's a very multi-racial, cosmopolitan area. People genuinely try to get on with each other. There is a general tolerance, except for those blues. A lot of the problems are the same for black and white. There are a lot of inter-racial relationships. The young ones aren't nearly as racist, because that's what they've been born to. They've accepted it. The old can be racist. They remember Britain as it was before.

'No, prostitution isn't a problem. It should be legalised. Like calling for a plumber. It's a service, like any other. It's never bothered me.'

'It wouldn't though,' I interjected, 'seeing as you're not a woman.'

'No, but I still think it should be legalised. It does more harm being under the surface.' He paused. 'A lot of people won't put Hillfields on their address, especially going for a job.

'The flats are so isolated. They're filing boxes in the sky. It's a system which cares nothing for the human being. People have been found dead in the flats, there for weeks. Suicides used to happen as well.

'There were some good things. I was on the eighth flour and in the summer I could see all the way over to Bagington airport and see the planes landing. I had a bird's eye view of the city. There was an old bloke who liked to sit on his balcony and drink and play his mouth organ. We used to have a good laugh sometimes and there was a fair bit of community spirit built up on a landing. The old don't tend to blame society, they blame the quality of people. They tend to look back and think things were better when they were younger. They're right to an extent, but society itself has degenerated in recent years. Man's regard for his fellow man has declined. I always look back at the old times and that means the Second World War to me and the atomic bombs on Hiroshima and Nagasaki. I think a lot died in man after that. No one from that time can preach to us, or moralise about today's society. But things have changed. I don't see any rosy future for society, the way things are going. It makes me think at times, it really does.'

WOOD END – PLANS FOR A POOL HALL

Elan took one side whilst Valbert took the other. Hillmorton Road was the main street through Wood End, the post-war council estate built on the northern extreme of the city, isolated and neglected. Elan knocked at the first door of the block. He knocked again. No answer. He went to the second. He knocked. Then again. No answer. Then to the third. This time, he heard a woman scream something at a child and then shuffle up to the door.

It flew open, revealing a woman dressed casually in only a nightie and dressing gown.

'Yes?' she said. Like most people on the estate, she was friendly and welcoming.

'I'm sorry to disturb you,' Elan said brightly. 'We're in the area and we're doing a survey. We want to open a pool and snooker hall in the area and want to know if you like the idea.'

'Yer what?'

He thought she might be deaf, so he leant forward and shouted at her.

'We're doing a survey.'

'I ain't deaf, you know.'

'Sorry.'

'What sort of survey? You ain't from the Housing are ya? I've been waiting for you to see to my back boiler for months. Wha's'is about you putting new central heating in? Why ain't I heard nothing about it?'

'We want a pool hall.'

'What, in my house?'

'No,' Elan said. 'Up by the shops. We want to use the old Co-op building what's been empty for years now. We want to make it into a place for kids to go. They ain't got nowhere to go up here.'

'What Co-op?'

'Up by the shops?'

'Oh, I never use it.'

'No, it's closed.'

'Why d'you ask me if I use it then?'

'I never. I said *we* want to use it.'

'Why you asking me then?'

'We think there might be a bit of noise, you see, and we're asking everyone what lives in the area if they'd mind a pool hall near them. See? At the moment, all the kids have to go into town for any entertainment, and that means a lot of busfares and everything.'

'Them busfares are terrible,' she said. 'There ain't no shops up here neither. Only that supermarket place. I'd never use that. The prices he charges! There's not one decent shop on the estate. I heard the chippie's closing an'all, ain't it? 'Cause of vandalism, or something. Them kids.' She was about thirty. She turned her head back inside the house to tell her Shaun to stop pulling the dog's tail.

'Come on in,' she offered. 'It's cold on the step.'

She led him into the lounge. The fire was on full, but the room still seemed cold. Her three-year-old son was sitting on the couch watching the T.V. A black and white mongrel growled at Elan from behind an armchair.

'Come over here,' the woman said. 'Feel that.'

He put his hand on the outside wall. It was cold and he could feel a draught actually going through the wall.

'Like mine,' he said. 'I can't heat my place for love nor money. It don't 'alf eat up the electricity. But here's our petition. We're asking everyone to sign it, to say they support the pool hall.'

'What we need's more shops.'

'Yea, I know, but also the kids around here ain't got nowhere to go at night. That's why there's so much trouble and graffiti and fights and everything. There ain't nowhere to go round here. We've talked to all the kids and they think it's a great idea an'all. They say we need planning permission an'all that sort of stuff, but I think they'll go for it.'

'What about the noise?'

'There won't be much. We won't allow no rowdy behaviour. It'll stop all them kids roaming the streets and getting into trouble. And it'll provide jobs for people in the area, ones what can handle any trouble. We want to stay open 'til one in the morning, but the Council won't allow it after nine-thirty. People need the evening entertainment. And it'll be for the old people an'all, not just kids. Look.'

He had a diagram of the pool hall on another sheet of paper on his clipboard.

'This is what it's about.' The woman came over and sat right beside him on the couch, leaning forward, her thigh touching his and her dressing gown revealing more than it should. It quite put Elan off his patter.

'Er . . . you see . . . all these here . . . no here, and here, they're like video machines and invader machines. These are pool tables. No here. That's a snooker table. Or is it that one? Anyway, these are the toilets and, next to them, we're going to have a snack bar thingie, you know, with seats around.'

Elan was eighteen. She really ought to cover herself up, he thought. He was on serious work. The weekly business management course hadn't prepared him for this.

'We've got a lot of support already.' He tried to move further along the couch, but he couldn't. 'Everyone's signed it. We've got eight hundred signatures already. Or is it nine hundred?' She was staring at him. 'Er, we want to involve the community. You know, have day-trips and entertainments. We're running it as a co-operative.'

'I thought the Co-op was closed,' she said.

'No. A co-operative, not the Co-op.'

The difference baffled her.

'It's when people get together to run a business and they all share in it.'

'I believe in sharing.' She was staring again. 'Want a drink?'

'Yes please,' he said, hoping a nice cup of tea might cool everything off. But she rose, opened the sideboard and poured some gin into two glasses.

'Want tonic?'

'Er . . . yes please.'

Then she sat back down beside him, knees up on the couch this time, leaning into the other arm, looking at him. He took a gulp at his gin.

'We've seen the pool hall in town,' he said, 'and the businesses what supply the pool tables and snacks from the wholesalers. We've worked out the prices and costs and overheads an' things. But a lot of money needs to be spent on the building itself.'

'Does it?'

'Yea. Ten or twenty thousand at least. And we've got to get the lease off of the other shopkeeper. We've got to plumb in the water an' all. I think he's hanging out for a better price. We'll have to have some sort of membership, so's we can check out who comes in.'

'Will I be allowed in?'

'Yea. Course. It'll only be over sixteen's, because the Council's worried in case there's more truancy from school. They say there's a lot in this area anyway.'

'I used to be a right devil at school,' she said.

'Did you?' He gulped again.

'I never saw the point in school.'

'Well, it don't get you no job at the end, does it. 'Specially up here. As soon's you says you're from Wood End, no employer wants to know ya. Nearly everyone's unemployed up here. I bet it's eighty per cent. I don't have no time for them government figures, they can't be right. They put everyone what's desperate for housing up here and then they leaves them to it.'

'There's only two shops and a bookies. Typical.' Her dressing gown was slipping down.

'And only one pub.'

'They should do something about that place. Have you seen it of a lunch time? It's packed. All spending their social.' She leaned closer to him.

'There ain't nothing else to do.' He was staring at the wall.

'Spend it on their kids, for a start.'

'Oh, they do. But it's to break the monotony, to get out. There ain't nowhere else to go round here.' He dropped his clipboard. It was a fatal mistake. She leant down to pick it up for him, revealing herself again.

'You're telling me. I go insane in this house all day.'

'Does your husband work?'

'He quit on me three years ago, duckie. A couple of sleepless nights with Shaun and he was off. Ain't seen him since.'

Elan swigged the rest of his drink.

'You sure people ain't going to just gamble away all their money?'

'There won't be no gambling machines.'

'Those invader machines are addictive though. My brother got through a hundred quid in an afternoon once. He started thieving and everything.'

'I don't think it'll be a problem. We'll organise social activites as well. It'll be like a club, with pool teams in the city leagues and lots of leisure games. But it's got to be a business as well. We've got to to be able to run it properly. All the kids round here are bored stupid. All the crime's due to that. Thieving's a fact of life up here. The police don't seem to care neither.'

'Some parts are no-go areas.'

'Yea.'

'So I should sign your petition?' She smiled.

'Yea, please.'

'And what do I get if I do?'

'A new pool hall, I hope,' he said.

'That all?'

'It'll be a lot of work.'

'You run a business before?' She took the sheet from him and wrote her address.

'Valbert, he's my partner, his brother ran a record shop in Hillfields for a while. But he went bust.'

'Oh.'

'But we're getting help from the Co-Operative Development Agency, for loans advice. And we've been on a business course dealing with tax and accounts, cash-flow, stock-taking, things like that.'

'Oh.'

'Here you are.'

She signed. Elan rose and made for the door.

'Call again,' she said, 'if you want anything.'

'Sure. Thanks.' He opened the front door, and, boy wasn't he glad to hit that street.

WOOD END - THE POSITIVE THINGS

Linda worked in the adventure playground at Wood End. She had just been over to the housing office and was walking back past the old council blocks which were now being knocked down. Men were on the roofs, breaking it up whilst, further along, others were ripping the plumbing and heating systems out of the maisonettes, stripping out the toilets and sinks and all the kitchen units and cupboards and throwing the wood onto large bonfires which were sending palls of black smoke into the sky.

It was hard to believe that people once lived in them, or that children once scampered across the bleak, barren areas of grass surrounding them. Without window frames, their no-fines concrete walls exposed their appallingly badly made structure. Pebbles. Walls made of pebbles, with hardly a lick of cement holding them together. As you touched them, they broke away in your hand.

On her right, as she dodged broken glass and wood splinters, was a barren area, bare to those winds which had always buffeted this end of the estate. Several more blocks had once stood there, being boarded-up for many years as even the most desperate for accommodation refused to live in the grim, dirty, freezing, end-of-the-world flats.

As she walked along, many of the blocks which were still inhabited had boards up over several of their flats as well. She knew that the boards over the windows of one ground-flour flat hid a couple squatting in the darkness.

The playgroup for the under elevens at the adventure playground would be starting soon, so she hurried on. It went on until six-thirty, giving them a chance on the pool and table-tennis tables, when five-year-olds, barely able to see over them, would shoot a game or two. Then at seven, things really started to hot up with the youth club.

Wood End was special to Linda. She had worked there for ten years. There was a real community spirit. People from the other areas ran Wood End down, but they'd never been there. All they ever heard about was the rubbish or graffiti or crime. A lot of the crime was not in Wood End anyway, but, because the whole policing area was termed "Wood End", it was labelled worse then it was. People thought that Wood Enders ate each other for breakfast. They thought the area was full of muggers, waiting along derelict paths: Darkest Wood End, where people entered and were never heard of again. But it annoyed her that they had never been there or seen it for themselves.

The reality was different. People always offered her a cup of tea when she went round. Doors were always open. At the time of the royal wedding, they'd had a huge street party and the last bonfire night had attracted a hundred and fifty people. Everyone was really friendly.

People didn't understand the situation up there. They had so little in the way of amenities or entertainments. There was only one pub, two shops, three telephone boxes and only a small community centre for an evening out. People had to make their own entertainment. The adventure playground had an unemployed group in the day and a regular music workshop, which had given birth to a reggae/heavy rock band and a couple of punk bands, which blasted out the room as men played pool and their pre-school children messed around with ping-pong balls or paints. It was a regular fathers' and toddlers' group. The kids had got up a petition to get the adventure playground open for longer hours and they'd talked about doing a youth magazine.

The rest of the community was the same. There was a flourishing writers' group, which had published two booklets. Some residents were performing a play about the Wood End area in Woodway Park, the local community school, with a bloke videoing it for them as well. On the What's On board in the playground building, there were plans for a number of activities, many of which were based at the Community Flat. There was a weekly trip to Woodway Park for pottery and dressmaking classes, a women's group in basic electrics, a men's group and invitations to the Outreach Centre, set up as a community focal point for discussing problems and helping people get their rights. The Urban Aid bid for an extension to and refurbishment of the Adventure Playground had just come through. The staff and the kids were full of exciting ideas for the place.

It was an atmosphere of enterprise amongst deprivation. A young lad who sniffed glue brought in some mice one day in a plastic bag. He had caught them in his flat and sold them around the other kids for fifty pence a time. During the summer play scheme, they had taken fifty kids strawberry picking. They had eaten the whole field and only taken seven pounds home.

They would take the kids swimming to get their certificates. They organised junior keep fit, discos and trips. On one trip, a barge journey, there had been one kid who had fallen in and another who had suffered an asthma attack in the middle of the night, disrupting the whole barge as they had searched for his inhaler.

There was poverty, a lot of it, but people made the best of it. It had been really brought home to her once. She had invited three little ones around to her house for tea one day. She told them they had to be good for a week and then they could come for tea. They were angels for seven days. They came round and she held a little party for them. It was the first time they had ever done it and one of them told her, 'You're the richest person we've ever seen.'

She had taken a group of ten fifteen and sixteen-year-olds into an Indian restaurant one lunchtime. They had never been in one before and had passed all sorts of racist comments about smelly breath and curry. In there, one boy had refused to take his coat off. 'I can't' he had said. 'I've got no buttons on my shirt.' They hadn't believed how smart it was. 'This,' said one, 'is the poshest place I've ever been.'

Some of their families were intensely deprived. Within the context of poverty, some made do and lived as neatly and respectably as they could. Others gave in under the pressure. One house you would go in would be a tip, without carpets and with dog excrement on the floor, alongside empty bottles and fag-ends. Another would be spotless, though showing signs of wear. People were people, wherever they were. Poverty broke some, whilst others struggled on.

She walked past the half-empty blocks further along Binton Road, past where the new elderly residential home was going to be built, past where the new housing estate was going to be and into Wappenbury Road.

School failed a lot of kids, but the teachers should come and see where they lived. How important was homework, when a kid might be hungry? So many never had breakfasts. There was also a lot of truancy, not helped by their parents having such bad experiences of school themselves and no confidence in the education system. It was a vicious circle.

Some kids had never seen the countryside either. A trip on a barge or a week in the Yorkshire Dales would be a once-in-a-lifetime experience. On one trip to the theatre, all the kids had rushed straight down to the front and she'd had to explain to them that they all had tickets and had to sit in the seats numbered on them.

As she turned up the drive to the adventure playground and through the wall which surrounded it, then past the climbing frames and play hill, to the solid-looking building which housed her office as well as the youth club and snack bar, she realised how attached she was to the area, how much she felt part of it. Kids she'd not seen for years would phone her up, asking for references, or inviting her to their weddings, or even for help, because their parents had evicted them.

It wasn't a job, it was a way of life. She didn't think of it as work. It was about people getting on together, learning to live together, and giving them the opportunity to do things for themselves.

She unlocked the heavy door, switched on the lights and settled herself in for another evening of wild and totally unpredicatable events.

BALL HILL AND STYVECHALE

George decided to go for a walk. Well, his wife decided for him actually. 'Get out of my hair,' she'd said. 'Go for a walk.' But what had really made his mind up was her remembering the garage door needed repainting. He was in no mood for that at all.

He put on his jacket and entered the warm June sunshine. The area he lived in was so different to the area where he worked, he thought as he turned along Belvedere Road, in the posh end of Earlsdon. Here it was all large houses, many detached, with large, secluded gardens and tree-lined streets. Behind Ball Hill, where he was the manager of a branch of an insurance company, it was street after street of old terraced housing, mostly with tiny front gardens.

In an area like Kingsway, where many of the houses were in desperate need of repair, or in the streets off Clay Lane, where the roads were packed tightly together, the gardens were small and it was all some owners could do to retain the fabric of the houses from the damp and cold.

He turned into Dalton Road, past the tennis courts and bowling green, past Spencer Park and up towards Henry VIII public school.

All Ball Hill and the streets around the football ground had were odd patches of playing area. There was a green at Gosford, a few swings and a football pitch at the Baths Park and a patch at Barras Heath. There were no sports facilities in these spaces at all.

He turned into the green along the Warwick Road and headed for The War Memorial Park, breathing in the clean aroma of pine trees and flower beds, under the cherry trees which, a month before, had been overwhelmed with blossom.

Ten years he'd been at the branch at Ball Hill. And quite content he was too. He was in his early fifties and wasn't keen to move on. He was settled and happy. But what distressed him was the deterioration he'd seen in Stoke over the years.

Although he was a branch manager, he wasn't unconcerned about the poor. It depressed him to see the disrepair, so what must it be like for the residents? People were finding it hard. The inner city areas were precisely those where unemployment hit most. Coventry had moved from near the top of the table for wages to near the bottom. The big growth area had been in part-time, low-paid work. It was an area where many men relied upon moonlighting for a few extra pounds. You wouldn't believe the number of window cleaners, off-the-record plumbers and electricians, nor the garden sheds emitting sounds of hammering and sawing.

He crossed the busy Warwick Road into The Memorial Park. A couple of joggers puffed past. Some dogs scampered over the acres of grass surrounding the azalias and rhododendrons. He strolled in the late afternoon sun, between the lines of cedars, past the bowling greens, towards the tennis courts.

He knew how people were getting into debt. His company demanded higher rates of insurance for some areas of Coventry, for household contents, because of the higher rate of crime there. In an area like Stoke, burglaries were rising and the number of people who could afford insurance was falling. Occasionally, someone would come in and ask if they arranged loans and have to be turned away. There was a cycle of debt some people never climbed out of. A lot of single women found themselves with expenses around their necks, or unable to afford the mortgage. It was a cycle of deprivation.

The children were out in the paddling pool and rushing around the slides and swings. Some kids on BMXs were racing between the trees. He gently walked along beside the cricket pitch and the families having a kick around. Someone had a kite he was trying to fly.

No, it was more like a spiral of deprivation. The problems and stress parents faced made it harder for the kids. The teachers had the stress of larger classes. Headmasters had to deal with more cases of abuse, truancy and family problems. It was all a growing weight and the kids remained deprived.

He turned out of the Park and crossed back over the Warwick Road to go down Beechwood Avenue. It led past common land and large spacious houses down to the golf course. George played a relaxing round every Sunday before dinner with some banking chums.

His own feeling of impotence frustrated him. So did the apathy of so many of the people around. Those in Stoke were unwilling to do anything about their situation and those in the clubhouse unconcerned about helping.

You couldn't say that they should help themselves, nor that they were just inferior human beings. They had been driven down to apathy by years of struggling and getting nowhere. Circumstances weren't random, they were engineered by the type of society we lived in. People weren't simply inadequate, it was that they couldn't cope with the pressures.

He smiled as he walked past the large open space of the course and cut through an entry smelling of honeysuckle, towards Earlsdon's shopping centre. His business colleagues complained of the pressures of management, but they had nothing to compare with some of the people along Brighton Street and the roads off it. Money bought a lot of freedom from cares. It made a lot of things an awful lot easier. And compared with some of the familes on low incomes, they had a lot of money, an awful lot. They spent more on their cars then a family of six spent of food.

In fact, he thought, walking down Stanley Road and turning into Earlsdon Street, when it came to strength of character, some of the characters in the clubhouse were pretty dubious. He'd like to see them live on eighty pounds a week.

He remembered walking one evening along Brighton Street and Heath Road, and passing all the Indian shops open until late and seeing the cars on the street, some big and flash, other rusting away. He had watched as young children ran to a shop to buy a few groceries, then back home again, their treat being a packet of sweets.

The shops in Earlsdon looked smart, clean and prosperous. Those on Ball Hill and dotted amonst the back streets, often looked poor and run-down. They were different worlds.

He turned up Earlsdon Avenue South. Individuals reacted differently.

No matter how similar two people's circumstances looked, they would be different, their previous experience would not be the same and the way they reacted wouldn't either. Some had outside interests, kept busy and had been brought up to be and look tidy. They were concerned to keep up appearances. Others may have given up trying to cope and not want to kowtow to the image of "coping" in hardship.

Was it nature or nurture? He had always thought that character was shaped by the enviroment anyway. It was both. An interplay, where only the fittest escaped from their situation. People weren't encouraged to develop their intellect and abilities. Many turned their backs. They *didn't want* to be told about it, they *didn't want* to be told how to cope with it, they *didn't want* to be patronised, to be offered charity or help. Their pride was all they had left and they only survived by not looking around.

It was as though all the ceilings in every house in the country were slowly getting lower. Everyone was different, each going about his or her business, but the ceilings were getting lower and eventually everyone ended up crawling around on the floor.

As he climbed the hill, George thought how the children seemed happier and healthier where he lived. The unemployed had more illnesses, their houses tended to be damper and less well insulated. Earlsdon had a good library, its streets were cleaner and safer and its gardens bigger.

He had seen people who had just given up on life. They were demoralised and felt totally powerless. They felt alone, forgotten, ignored. They were gradually degraded until anyone could do anything they liked with them. They had lost their sense of humanity. They hid away from the world. The next bill dominated their thoughts. They often lived in fear and their lives were fraught with difficulty after difficulty.

It made him despair, it really did.

He turned back into Belverdere Road. He fancied a nice cup of tea and some chocolate cake in his back garden.

STOKE ALDERMOOR – BRENDAN

Brendan had lived in Stoke Aldermoor for twenty years. He had come to Coventry as a young man from Liverpool and had worked for Coventry Climax, the forklift truck manufacturers, at their assembly plant in Radford. He had married a local woman and they had been given a maisonette in the Pondfield. As it had been a very cold block, he had put in for a transfer and been given a three-bedroomed house on Roundhouse Road, by the shops. It was an older property, built between the wars, warmer than the other place and had its own front and back garden.

He now worked at Talbot's Stoke plant, on sub-assembly. There had been a lot of redundancies there and for many years now, the shadow of complete closure had been hanging over them. So far, it had been staved off.

He had heard that The Pondfield was being done up by the Council, to be sold off to a housing association. So much council property was being sold, yet the average person couldn't care less. Some felt that more private houses on the estate would balance out the council housing.

Until recently, the estate had been allowed to deteriorate, but now a major refurbishment scheme was in operation. Houses were being given proper gardens, the garages, bulk-bin areas and sheds were being done up, the houses were being repainted, new fences were being erected and there was a general tidying-up campaign. Over in The Boxhill, a day-centre had been set up for families in need, with a full-time adviser. It all seemed a bit superficial, though, to Brendan.

The estate was in two parts. The old estate had been built in the thirties and forties, consisting of terraces of brick houses with front and back gardens. The new estate, built in the fifties, was of the disastrous no-fines concrete. The old estate had a high proportion of elderly who had lived there since the estate had been built, but also had new, young families moving in to replace them.

Quite a few people had left the estate in the last few years. A lot of them had worked for Talbot's or the G.E.C. There had been the "twilight shift", when women would walk to work for a four o'clock start. There used to be droves of them, going to assemble parts for telephone exchanges. Now unemployment was very high on the estate effecting something like a third of eligible men and three-quarters of women. In fact, women's employment in the city had drastically fallen recently, though it hadn't been as dramatic as the closures in the car factories. As a result, many people who had migrated to Coventry had gone back home to be with their families.

It was even worse for the youth. All they had were Y.T.S., Community Programme jobs and working for the black economy as picture sellers, window cleaners or for scrap dealers. Some of them turned to crime, stealing whole central heating systems from empty council properties. Before, criminals had been older, more "professional" and had at least had the moral code of thieving from the better-off areas and never on their own patch. Now, for the teenage criminal, every neighbour was a potential victim.

It was logical in a system which encouraged "individuality", "enterprise", "the survival of the fittest", and selfishness. Where did that stop? You were told you could survive if you worked hard enough, but, without work, it became survival if you stole hard enough. It was how they saw the ethos of society. It didn't do anything for them, so why should they do anything for it. They often see their parents reduced to passive acceptance of their plight, but youth won't be passive, they won't just accept it. Most crime on the estate was by eleven to fifteen year olds.

'Where had all the care gone in Britain?' he wondered.

Some of the kids joined gangs, where the ability to steal more audaciously than the rest became a matter of pride and respect. It was a cauldron, waiting to boil over.

With many of the middle-aged people leaving, there were a lot of old and young, but not so many in-between. As those tended to be the moral guardians and the most self-confident, it left the kids relatively unsupervised. It was the same for the city centre. Only kids went in at night. There was nothing for middle-aged people.

When parents worked long hours, or when teachers faced large classes, it undermined authority, made it harder to keep an eye on youngsters and bring them up properly. For those fathers out of work, the problem was that some of them lost the respect of their children. There were also a fairly large number of single-parent families around as well.

Financial pressures were the greatest. He knew about that himself. He had been unemployed for two years after losing his job at the Climax. He had been lurching from bill to bill. He had lost his self-esteem and confidence. They had been continually in financial problems and had been in trouble over a provident clothing debt.

So he knew what it was like. He knew the pressure of glossy ads and kids wanting expensive toys at Christmas. It was what he dreaded happening again and why he would never go on strike or jeopardise the factory. It was a terrible fear.

There had been nothing for him to do. There hadn't been the schemes in those days. Now, the community centre had a voluntary group support unit and a furniture renovation scheme. They made and repaired playschool toys in a workshop, employing quite a few people, and on decent wages as well.

Apathy had hit him badly at the time. He had never given up looking for a job, but had sunk into a sort of lethargy. He had been out in the garden a lot for the first few months, quite enjoying the sunshine and the rest, but that had soon bored him. He hadn't been able to motivate himself, believing there was nothing he could do about his situation. All his thoughts had become negative and depressing. Any constructive activity, like painting the bathroom or going to the shops had felt like an enormous effort. He had become overwhelmed with his own problems, a lot of them imagined or blown out of proportion as he had sat and brooded over them. Even shaving had been too tiresome. He had tried joining the residents' association, but had soon become fed-up with that as well. It couldn't change anything, not really.

Something else he had noticed was how dependent he had become on bureaucracies like social services or housing. It had been horrifying to think that any week the D.H.S.S. could stop his money for any reason and he could have faced starvation. He had felt himself becoming totally dependent on others' whims and had found it humiliating beyond words having to queue up at the employment exchange and the social security office to fill in forms to get a pittance to live on.

One good thing was that some people on the estate had set up a credit union to stop people having to go to the loan sharks all the time. They paid in about one-fifty a week. It didn't solve every problem, but it helped pay the bills and to buy Christmas presents. It also gave back to people some financial control over their lives.

The estate could look so dreary on a wet winter's evening. There was nothing to do except the pub. For kids, there was school, then nothing. Again, the exception was the community centre, which ran club camping weekends, competitions and adventurous activities like midnight hikes. It had its own minibus which was a great advantage. The centre also ran activities for parents with young children. There was a latch-key service and, in the summer holidays, there was a playscheme for them. They had a toy library and a crèche, and both a parents' and toddlers' group and a play group. But people looked grey and barren. They needed cheering up, they needed life, they needed some community spirit.

The local festival was always good. It lasted a week in June or July. It ran competitions, sports events, a ramble, morris dancing, barbecues, quizzes, discos and even a teddy bears' picnic. It involved the whole community – schools, churches and local groups, culminating in a Grand Gala on Saturday with a street parade in fancy dress, marching bands, side shows, stalls and cars decorated with bunting and ribbons.

There was a loyalty to Stoke Aldermoor underneath, which occasionally sharply showed itself, as when a street party was held for a young girl with a fatal disease to go to Disneyland. Yet it was never a long-lasting thing. It was always a sudden burst which petered out.

Community spirit comes from pride in your area and when it looks dreary and in disrepair, people lose their enthusiasm. It costs a lot to decorate a house and look after a garden. Leisure costs money. Without money, it becomes oppressive.

If you haven't a decent pair of trousers, you can't go out, or go to the pub and buy a round. Getting involved in groups costs as well. You can't have pride in your community without pride in yourself. You might be swept along briefly during the festival, but it wouldn't last. Apathy erodes the community spirit as well. People don't want to know, they are too busy worrying about next week's bills and the damp in the kitchen.

There was a growing gap where many local initiatives were either stamped on or taken over by professionals, so people felt isolated and without a say. They became reliant on others doing things for them. Any plan they put forward had to get planning permission, there were numerous meetings to attend, forms to fill in, officials to see. It was an idea amongst bureaucrats that they had to retain control, that things had to be from the top down, all filling some monster plan or other. This in turn was all being squeezed by the lack of money available as resources were cut.

But he had noticed some successes. The estate was looking better, people were more cheerful recently, and a few local initiatives had been successful, like the application for a new community centre. The Stoke plant *was* still open, there was still life to lead. It might be because City won the cup, and because the sun was shining, but he hoped it proved to be a more profound change.

"WHAT YA GONNA DO ABOUT IT?"

The street representatives started drifting into the hall of the community centre to sit and chat behind the tables pulled into a line opposite Clair McManus, the chairwoman.

'Right,' she said, 'let's get down to it. We've not much time today. I've asked Lynn Hanson, the Area Housing Officer, to come in half an hour. Now, we need specific details of repairs and complaints. It's no use being too general. We must have addresses.'

She looked around the members of the Wood End Tenants' Association. The hall was a bit cold as it was March. It had been built by the tenants themselves, with their own money, the only one like that in the city. It had all been possible with the great community spirit in Wood End, with sponsored walks, gala days for the kids, jumble sales and a sponsored walk to Rugby and back in fancy dress. They had received some Urban Aid money, but the foundations and drains had been done voluntarily by young people. The youth on the estate were fantastic, when you conceded that there was nothing for them on the estate other than the Adventure Playground.

The community had also set up a number of its own groups. There was one for pensioners and another for mothers and toddlers. They had built the Adventure Playground and raised money for a B.M.X. cycle track.

The atmosphere amongst the people, was, at times, very good. It *was* a community. Many people had lived there a long time and were proud of the estate. The real problems were concentrated in only a few roads, although nearly every house faced the need for some repair. For many people, their doors were always open and they felt a strong desire to help each other out. The deprivation of the area had affected some of the tenants by encouraging them into joint efforts to improve things themselves. The community had its leaders. They were the ones who *did* get up and do things, who actively worked to improve the conditions. However, the majority of people kept themselves to themselves. Many were knocked back by the state of the area. A group of tenants had come together to express their feelings in a play, about the area, and rehearsed it into shape. It reflected the humour as well as the grimmer reality of life the estate.

Clair was still taking addresses of people with complaints.

'Me guttering's gone,' said Mr Brown, an elderly gentleman.

'What number are you Tom?'

'Twenty-three.'

The Housing Officer was soon invited in, along with a man from the Council Repairs Department.

'What ya gonna do about my guttering?' Tom asked in a loud voice.

'Wait a moment, Tom,' Clair interrupted. 'We'll deal with that in a moment.'

Lynn introduced herself and, at the beginning, told the tenants how much she and the Council sympathised with the difficulties they faced and how the Council was as disappointed with the standard of housing which had been built by the contractors in Wood End in the fifties as the tenants were, and how it was desperately doing as much as it could to raise the estate to an acceptable standard.

Clair started the questions on the issue of the local Co-op supermarket, which had been the only large shop on the estate, but which had been closed for years. The tenants' association had made an application for it to be turned into a non-profit making community-run hall, full of stalls and a launderette.

'The Council doesn't own the lease,' Lynn said. 'And the present owner runs the grocer's next to it.'

'What about an Urban Aid grant to buy it and do it up?'

'You can try.'

'We need more shops here. It's terrible. And the prices are so high. Aren't any more shops being built as part of the refurbishment plans?'

In reply, the Housing Officer described how the old estate was going to be given a face-lift, some of the blocks knocked down and new housing built. Clair sat back smoking a cigarette, listening and occasionally keeping order.

A few people on the estate had lost their sense of worth and had become totally uninterested in anything taking place around them. Some had gradually lost their motivation as powerlessness and an inability to escape their situation had sunk in. They, just like the houses and flats, were the product of long-term neglect, long-term unemployment and a lowering of expectations. They weren't used to being asked their opinion, or of it being listened to, or of it having any effect whatsoever. That was why there was often a low turn-out to public meetings. People felt powerless, that it was all a complete waste of time and effort. And apathy lead to passivity.

The residents lacked both confidence in themselves and in the Council. The answer had been to take the improvement plans to them. Lynn Hanson herself saw her role as building a better relationship with the tenants and restoring some pride and interest in the area. So Council employees had knocked on every door, to involve them and interest them, because they were the ones who would have to try and keep it looking better once the plans were finished. Now the workers were on-site, interest was rising.

The intention was to build a sheltered block for elderly people, have a new private housing estate and to give more people their own gardens, with precise boundaries. "Definable space" were the watch-words now. The Council would also build four new blocks of houses and refurbish the remainder with uPVC windows, gardens, fencing, new rendering on the outside, better front-door access, rewiring, central heating, better street lighting and landscaping.

Someone mentioned the new outside doors being fitted by the contractors. Tom interrupted again.

'What ya gonna do about my back door?' he asked. 'All the water from the guttering's getting in and rotting it. I thought you were replacing all the doors.'

'My back window's held in by three nails,' another tenant said.

'They've left two window frames in my back garden, but ain't done the windows,' said another.

'They've done one of mine, but not the other. I've got the rain coming in through it.'

'What ya going to do about my guttering?' Tom insisted. 'They've put a new door frame in, but left the rotten door.'

'There's a half inch gap over the top of my balcony door, letting all the cold in,' yet another reported.

The Housing Officer noted all the complaints and promised they would be passed on to the private contractors and tried to explain all the repairs they would be doing. She was doing a good job in the face of the enormous problems the area had. The Council itself had felt badly let down by the no-fines properties and recognised the mistake of building them. It was now a matter of trying its best to repair the damage, but it would be a long, hard slog. Many of the repairs were being done by sub-contractors and the Council was not entirely happy with the service, finding itself somewhat in the middle, between the tenants and the contracted workmen.

'They left glass panes in my front garden for weeks, and I've little kiddies. It ain't right.'

Many of the tenants felt that Wood End had been poorly built. The flats, maisonettes and houses had been built with untreated wood which was now rotting, old-fashioned cisterns and enamel sinks, back-boilers and open fires and on foundations of shale slag from the nearby pits which had resettled and swollen, pushing up the floors and cracking the walls.

'What ya gonna do about my guttering?' Tom inquired again, more loudly now. 'Me wall's all damp and it's coming in a crack and ruining me wallpaper.'

'My door's splitting.'

'What address?'

She was given the number in Lapworth Road.

'There's all black fungus growing,' mumbled Tom.

'They took away the old rotting doorstep,' a resident said, 'which was fine. Trouble is, the new one's not so big, so there's a gap between it and my carpet now.'

'We've been waiting three months for a new letterbox.'

'What's the address?' Lynn was given it, then she asked, 'Have you been sent a repair card?'

'Yes, it says within thirteen weeks.'

'Well, it's any time up 'til then, then.'

'It's alright for you, you haven't got a gale blowing through your hall.'

'Why on earth do they do the external repairs in the winter?'

'They have to work all year.'

'Why not inside work in the winter, though?'

'Because that's a different firm.'

'Seems daft to me.'

'And me floor's coming up in the front room,' Tom complained. 'It's all the damp from the broken guttering's doing it.'

'We're in the process of putting new uPVC windows in all the Council homes in the next fourteen years. We're doing all the rewiring as well, and installing new central heating.'

'Can you make sure they don't rewire mine on Wednesday, Thursday or Friday afternoons?' an elderly woman asked.

'Why not?'

'It's Sons and Daughters.'

'What ya gonna do about my back door? There's a crack with the wind blowing through,' Tom grumbled.

'I asked for my toilet to be replaced years ago, but I haven't had a card.'

'What's the address?' She was told. 'Ah yes. It's on-screen on the computer. You should've had a card.'

'Well, I haven't.'

'I'll look into it.'

'Are you changing our fires?'

'No. Well, it depends on the age of the property and the condition it's in.'

'Mine's fifteen years old,' Tom replied. 'And,' he added, 'what ya gonna do about them stray dogs on the estate?'

'That's not Housing, Mr Brown.'

'It is when they pee on my wall.'

Most of the homes were built with heating which was not adequate for the no-fines problems. The walls were so poor that heating bills were enormous and the walls ran with condensation.

Those houses in Tachbrook Close and River Walk, which were facing the River Sowe and the wind howling across the open fields, were very cold and exposed. The health of tenants was noticably worse than elsewhere in the city, with a higher rate of respiratory diseases, such as bronchitis, asthma, pleurosy and pneumonia.

Poverty in itself brought illnesses like polio and tuberculosis. The roofs of the houses had little insulation and some of the ventilators in the windows didn't close properly, forcing some tenants to use paper to block them. Also, the internal doors were hardboard-cavity ones which tended to warp and let out the heat.

'What ya gonna do about my drain?' Tom wanted to know. 'It's been blocked for ages. That's why the guttering's broke, with all the water in it. It smells something terrible.'

'It stinks, don't it Tom.'

'Terrible, terrible.'

'A lot of people are complaining about the new central heating,' Clair said. 'The pumps are breaking down and people are complaining that they're paying for it on their rents, but haven't got it.'

'We're doing the best we can,' Lynn replied. 'There are bound to be some hiccups in any programme.' Hers was an impossible situation. She sympathised with the tenants, but there weren't the resources since the Government had drastically cut the money it gave to local authorities for housing.

'I'll look into the matter of the pumps once more,' she added. 'What's the address? We've got a rolling programme to completely refurbish every one of the two thousand properties on the estate.'

'How many each year?'

'Two hundred and fifty. It's the best we can do. We can't afford any more, because of the tight limits on the housing budget. The Council isn't building any more houses at all. It can't afford to. All it can do is refurbish existing stock. We're trying to give priority to those with families. Wood End has a larger slice of the budget for central heating than other parts of the city.'

'It needs it.'

'Yes, but there are thirteen thousand no-fines properties in Coventry, of which only two thousand are in Wood End. and the multi-storey blocks have their own problems with under-floor heating. The problems the Council faces are staggering.'

'What about the dogs?' Tom repeated. 'They hang around my drain.'

'People just throw their rubbish on the open spaces. They dump their old cars. Then we get fires and glass everywhere.'

'The cars get vandalised, then abandoned.'

'People can't afford to take their old furniture to the tip. They haven't got cars, so they dump it.'

'The dogs get into the black bin bags and empty the rubbish all over the pavement.'

'We need another clean-up campaign.'

'They collected 460 tonnes of rubbish last time.'

'Never!'

'Yea. Shows the need, don't it.'

'When you say families are getting priority, what's a family?'

'A family-sized unit. Houses mainly.'

'But some young couples are in maisonettes and've as much right to central heating.'

'But in some, we have to rewire first. The wiring's so bad, it wouldn't be worth putting in new fires until then.'

'What ya gonna do about my guttering?' Tom asked again. 'All them dogs keep ripping up my bin bags. Now some joker's dumped an old mattress there as well.'

'When the contractors do repairs, they don't do other little jobs, like repairing other fires, because it isn't on their sheets.'

'I've complained about the standard of repairs. They left big holes in the walls.'

'They shouldn't have,' Lynn sympathised.

'But when I complained, I was sent from one department to another. No one seems to know what anyone else's doing.'

'Leave it with me,' Lynn said. 'What's the address?'

'My water's not been on for six weeks,' one said.

'I've got plenty,' Tom interrupted. 'Come over, and bring a bucket.'

'Why's it take so long for repairs?'

'The system isn't perfect,' Lynn said.

'You never know who to complain to.'

'For the first year, it's the contractor. After that, it's the main contractors employed by the Council to service all the heating in the city.'

'I haven't got a thermostat to control the heat.'

'One pensioner had no pump for three weeks in January.'

'Next door to me, their immersion caught fire. They were the warmest for months. But then their electricity was all shut off. This is since January as well.'

'Once I told them we'd get our own contractor in and bill them,' Clair said. 'They were there before I got back from the phone.'

'If it's the boiler or fire,' Lynn Hanson said, 'it's the main contractor's responsibility. If it's a broken pipe, it's the Council's. The main contractor should make the *initial* response within twenty-four hours, but there may be a delay with the parts. There's a phenomenal pressure on Council Repairs in January.'

'Yes,' Clair added, 'the Council does its best. But will you raise these points with the contractors?'

'Yes, indeed.'

The people in Wood End felt they had been forgotten, stuck right out at the end of the No. 21 bus route, miles from town, decent shops and decent entertainments. They felt they had been ignored. Most were very keen on the new plans for the estate, though they knew it would only solve some of their problems, because the high levels of people on supplementary benefit and unemployed, especially the youth, would still be with them.

Vandalism would continue to be a problem, as would the amount of crime on the estate and the availability of drugs. It was, for some, the "never known" syndrome. The youth had never known bushes, flowerbeds and trees before and weren't used to them. It was essential to gradually create an atmosphere where all these things *were* accepted and protected and *weren't* a target for graffiti and window-breaking.

The Council was also trying to counter the lack of services and facilities on the estate with a new family support unit, providing space for get-togethers and perhaps with a family centre. They were also revamping the small row of shops and giving support to plans of some local youth for a pool hall and coffee bar in the centre of the estate.

'Right,' Clair McManus said, 'we'd better draw everything to a close. Are there any more points to raise before I close the meeting?'

The Housing Officer looked around.

'There's just one thing,' Tom said. 'What ya gonna do about my guttering?'

The Independent Order of Foresters

213

ON THE BINS

Mick clocked on at seven-thirty in the morning, then went up to the canteen to wait for the rest of the Round 10 gang to come in. He was the chargehand and greeted them as they arrived. Two of them that day would be spare men taken out of the pool, to cover for one man absent and another on holiday. When they were called, Mick and the others walked out to their wagon and Alf drove them off to their round. It was Tuesday, so they would start in Whitley, then move on to Willenhall.

As it was raining heavily by the time they arrived, they put on their orange weather-proofs, before clambering out of the cab. Each man took a pile of black bags, ripped a large hole in one, threaded his arm and head through, making it into a sling, then slung the rest of the bags across it. One of them wore a whole bin-bag over his head and shoulders like a large hood, covering all of his back.

Working up and down the small side streets, four would go down the entries, bring out the large bags and stack them into piles every twenty yards or so, whilst Chalkie threw them onto the back of the wagon, helped by Alf.

They were part of an extremely efficient service the Council provided to cater for the whole city. Mike and the others had seen many changes, but the quality, Mick felt, had steadily improved.

The wagon was a new Dennis, holding about four tonnes of rubbish. It had to make three trips to the Waste Reduction Unit each day to be emptied, depositing about two and a half loads altogether. That amounted to at least ten tonnes of rubbish a day. Over the city as a whole, the binmen shifted sixty-two thousand tonnes a year. In a day, each man walked an estimated fifteen miles. It was extremely physically demanding, hunking heavy bags those sort of distances, an occupation not made easier by the weather.

When it rained, they would get soaked with sweat underneath their waterproofs. They had to go out no matter what the conditions, even in the snow. Summer wasn't as bad, of course, when there was one. Then their heavy coats would be shed, their sleeves rolled up and they could soak up the sun instead of the rain.

Mick walked down an entry with about five back gates along it, several with stiff or awkward bolts to pull open. He cleared out the dustbins and replaced the lids where they had been blown off or simply not put back, thus allowing the bin-bag to become sodden in the downpour. He pushed a new bin-bag through the handle of each lid, picked up two extra bags left by a gate and staggered back to the street, to dump them in a pile on the pavement.

Down the next entry, he reached over the first gate to unbolt it. A terrier leapt up and snapped at his hand, just missing his fingers as he pulled them sharply away. Several men on that round had been caught by that animal, mostly spares who didn't know the area and hadn't made mental notes of every vicious dog on the round.

Pensioners' bags tended to be smaller, especially if they were living on their own, perhaps with a little garden waste and often a few small cans of pet food. There would be signs of saving as well, with packet soups instead of tins, or smaller tins and packets. Some people could afford mounds of junk food and their bins would be full of chocolate wrappers, wine bottles, Marks and Spencer quiche wrappings and a great deal of waste food. Others seemed to never buy anything unnecessary at all.

Down some entries, they worked as a team, clearing every house, then all going down the next one. Along other streets, two would do each side, leap-frogging, with the driver and Chalkie loading the bags.

They quickly finished the few streets in Whitely and climbed back in to drive off to Willenhall, starting from near the London Road and working their way over, past the Willenhall shops, to Tarquin Close.

Kevin and Willie were spares. They were standing in for men who were absent from the team. One was on his holidays and the other had been run over by the wagon. As it had reversed, he had slipped and his foot had been caught and squashed under the wheel. It hadn't been the first accident on the round. People were always throwing away tins without pushing the lids in, or putting broken glass in without wrapping it up. One man's arm had been ripped open by a can from his wrist to his elbow, as he had thrown a bag into the wagon. On another team, a bloke had broken his ankle and been off for months. He might never be able to do a round again.

As a team, they discussed every issue imaginable. Today, it was the Falklands War and the sinking of the Belgrano. As they reached Stretton Avenue and piled out, the rain eased, nearly stopping as they worked down Gunton Avenue, Knightlow and Dunsmore. Mick and Kevin turned down the top end of Stretton and did Fawley Close.

As Mick bent down to open one of the front cupboards where the bins

215

were kept, he jumped back in fright. A large rat, the size of a cat, scrambled out of the bin and pelted across the road into the back of another row of houses. After taking some deep breaths to recover from the shock, he braced his knee against the bin and gingerly pulled out the bag. It was ripped where the rat had chewed its way in. Despite having been cut several times, he didn't wear gloves, so had to be doubly careful. There was no point in them. They were no protection and, in this weather, became soggy, sticky and unbearable in a few minutes.

Kevin, meanwhile, had stopped and was looking at a small magazine he'd found in one of the bags.

'Here Mick, come over and see this,' he said.

Mick walked over. It was a hard porn magazine.

'Oh yea,' said Mick, 'you'd be amazed. Piles of them get thrown out. People throw out gold rings or even trusseaux boxes.'

'Never?' Kevin said. 'Number twelve wasn't done,' he added.

'Why not?'

'I couldn't open the door. It was stuck. I don't see why I should strain my back trying to open it, if they can't be bothered to.'

'O.K.' said Mick. As the chargehand, he was responsible for all the problems that arose and any bins not emptied. If they missed one, there could be trouble. Some residents could get very upset if their rubbish wasn't collected.

Kevin had been on spare for a while now. Usually, after two or three years, spares were offered a permanent round. Then, if the chance came up, they would try to get on rounds where they lived, so they could be dropped off near home after their shifts.

They worked their way down Wolsey Street, behind the Willenhall shopping precinct. People lived above the shops and sometimes dogs found a way into the backs and ripped open the bags. There weren't that many dogs around today, because of the rain, but on a sunny day, whole packs would follow them. They were dangerous and a health hazard. Mick felt like giving them a good boot at times, but had to restrain himself.

Although it was a messy job and a heavy one, he would never go back to the boredom of a factory. It had changed a great deal over the years. The black bin-bags made the job lighter and cleaner and the wages had caught up considerably on industry's. On the other hand, whilst a round used to be of about 250 dustbins a day, now they had to clear over 1,300 bags. There had been forty four-man crews at one time, but now there were only twenty-one five-man crews, and five of those worked the bulk bins. The wagons were also much bigger, up to sixteen tonnes laden.

'Not that one Kevin,' said Mick. 'They don't pay.' Kevin dropped the bag back. Shops and businesses were not part of the round, unless they paid to have their rubbish collected. They either had a bulk bin or blue bin bags. If they didn't pay, the men were forbidden to collect the rubbish, because, even if it had been done in all innocence, there would be the suspicion of them receiving a back-hander for it.

A few years ago, some of the men had been so keen to rush the job, that they had arrived at work in trainers. To stop that, and in an effort to improve the quality of the service, as well as a concern for the number of foot injuries suffered by the men, the management now issued them with boots.

It was best to let the teams have some leeway to do the job the most efficient way they could. Each packed a week's work in, covering approximately five thousand properties a week, depending on the amount of walking they had to do, so deserved to finish a little early each day. In a year, the teams distributed six and a half million bin-bags, and some of those full bags could weigh a hundredweight.

They walked into Lysander Street, still behind the shops. The wagon came up behind them. Alf would stop the wagon at each pile of bags, push the button in the cab which primed the ram, get out, help throw some bags on, then press the button for the hopper to bring the ram down, engorge the bags and thrust them up inside. He had been a spare for eight years himself, since finishing as a long-distance lorry driver. He liked the new Dennis wagons. They were quieter, more powerful and had a better ram. Each had a place for a short-wave radio, very useful in emergencies.

Kevin called Mick over again. One of the bags was heavy with something stinking. The smell was overpowering and sickening. Mick opened it and a swarm of flies flew out. Inside were animal skins, covered in maggots.

'Oh, not again.' Mick closed it and turned away. 'Something should be done about him.'

'What was it?' Kevin asked.

'Cat and rabbit skins. We've seen them before. He keeps hundreds of animals. They're all in a state. He doesn't look after any of them. He

217

must eat them, or something. I'm pretty sure he does some poaching as well.' He was grimacing with the thought of it.

'We should report him to the R.S.P.C.A.'

'Yea. What number is it?' Mick noted the address and decided to inform the foreman when he came round.

The smell was one of the worst things about the job, especially in the summer, with the bags crawling with maggots. Also, even when it was sunny, the bags could still be wet from rain which had fallen days before and the water could soak his trousers and get into his boots. Cats seemed to like peeing on them as well.

Some parts of the round were very unclean, others very clean. Was it that places went downhill, or the people? Mick felt it was both. In the nice districts, with drives and detached houses, residents would leave their bags by the pavement for them. They would also complain bitterly if they were missed or if some refuse was spilt onto the pavements. Their houses had well-defined boundaries, there were no packs of dogs or greens which no-one looked after or owned and no communal refuse areas where several families put their rubbish and which again were not anyone's responsibility.

On other estates, the story could be different. Often, people hadn't the money to keep their gardens neat and tidy and there might not be an electric mower amongst them. There was high unemployment and, due to the layout of the states and frustration of the youth, higher crime and vandalism. Some parents had lost their self-respect and the respect of their children.

One bloke he'd spoken to in Stoke Aldermoor had said it was all to do with despair. People gave up hope of a job, he reckoned. The youth would hang around, looking for trouble. They didn't seem to give a damn for an area which didn't seem to give a damn for them. It was like the riots. People never rioted in other people's areas, only their own.

In some parts of the city, the condition of the roads and pavements were something those living in the better-off areas would never tolerate. There was often an air of decay and neglect. The houses would be old or badly-built, with damp and rotting woodwork. People often couldn't afford to buy new carpets, let alone garden fencing or a gate.

The communal bins, where no-one had direct responsibility for them, were often disgusting. Bags were left for dogs to get at and sometimes they would find old washing machines or settees just dumped there. But there again, on those estates, fewer people had cars to take the stuff away themselves and couldn't afford to have it removed. Cleanliness was not next to godliness. It was next to money.

True, some people – a few – were absolute pigs. But they weren't the reason for the general deprivation of an area, just a further symptom, thrown there because they had failed to pay the rent or been so desperate they had been prepared to take a hard-to-let property. Even if they did tidy it all up, take away all the old mattresses, pick up all the litter, remove all the old tyres and sweep up the broken glass, it would be back as it had been within a month. They were areas deprived of resources and with people similarly deprived. Many coped excellently, keeping their homes spotless, but a few cracked and they made it bad for everyone else.

Alf worked the wagon up the shops. Then he left to take the first load to the Waste Reduction Unit for it to be burned. As he turned into Remembrance Road, he saw a knot of men waiting for "The Winnall" pub to open.

There were less people in the city now, Alf reflected, but more properties. Families were getting smaller and the elderly were living longer. The average size of a household was now less than three. It meant the rounds were getting longer, though the increase in the amount of rubbish was only slight. The main changes were all the packaging there was these days and the increase in vegetable and organic matter. On the other hand, the amount of cinders had gone down as more people had had electricity or gas put in.

He drove onto the weighbridge, then reversed up to the enormous holder containing hundreds of tonnes of rubbish ready for incineration. He descended from the cab and pressed the throttle and tailgate-raise buttons simultaneously to clear the tailgate. Then he pressed the throttle again and pulled the lever which activated the hydraulic ram to push the huge extractor plate back and force out the refuse. It tumbled down into the huge holder. He pressed the two buttons at the back of the truck to rotate the hopper in the tailgate, in case any refuse was caught in it, then lowered the tailgate and drove off, back to Willenhall.

He was the only one in the gang to get regular overtime, being allowed half an hour in the morning to check over the wagon and fifteen minutes at night to park it up and check for faults. It was statutory. Also, in winter, he was a stand-in for the gritting lorries. He carried a bleeper on him from November through to March and could be called at any time, usually at night.

He arrived at the spot he had left the crew. Chalkie was there and they started to throw the bags on, moving from pile to pile along the closes off Mary Slessor Street. Alf had to be careful as he reversed down each one.

City Engineers had a number of schemes going to encourage people to keep their area clean. They did displays and had an information caravan which toured the city. They did talks at schools and gave out certificates. They had a litter-free zone scheme and a litter prevention competition for the schools, run in the "Evening Telegraph". In conjunction with the residents' associations and the litter liaison staff, they would organise community clean-ups and sponsored litter pick-ups. There were also Public Health Action Areas, where, for a week, they would go round schools and factories, provide a can bank and, in some areas, provide a free skip for people to dump their rubbish.

They finished Tarquin and Fabian, then worked along the closes down Robin Hood Road, finishing in time for lunch. They felt cold and hungry as they pulled themselves up into the cab and took off their weatherproofs relieved for the rest as Alf drove back to the Foleshill Road depot, and glad for another chance to wind him up about the Argentinians. The rain pelted down outside, turning to a cold and aggressive hail.

TARQUIN CLOSE NÉ IVY WALK

Several cars are drawn up
Before the long block of flats;
The new porches blink in the sun.
Through the back, past bulk bins,
New tarmaced areas have kids playing,
Flapping, slapping laundry,
And the odd mongrel sunning herself.
An old mattress serves as a trampoline,
Two women talk at a backdoor,
A young man has his motorbike
Spread out over his yard
And the 2.30 to London clickety-clacks past,
Zipping along the embankment nearby.
The cream-wash rendering
Sparkles from the distance,
But flakes from close-by.

On the balcony a man and woman kiss,
Getting a suntan in the heat;
A T.V. can be heard from a flat
And an argument from another,
But peace soon repaints
Its passive colours over them all.

Others want to mould them, shape them,
Make them something they're not;
They want to hide the scars,
Disguise the emotional turmoil,
Operate upon their faces and not their hearts,
Plastic surgery to beautify them
In others' eyes and not their own,
Graft their individuality onto safety,
Erase the boldness of their statement,
Conceal the strength of their lament,
Rub down the edges of their bitterness
And turn them from a sword for others' minds,
To prisoners within their own.

So planners have called you Tarquin Close,
When once you were Ivy Walk,
Have given you the once-over,
Like some spent-out hag,
Bought you some new lipstick
And moved on.

THREE SCENES

(I)

Walking down from Spencer Park, from the plane trees, dogs and kites, I stroll under a railway bridge along Albany Road in Earlsdon. I notice some advertising hoardings. One proclaimes the needs of the Children's Society and Dr Barnardo's. Opposite it, another announces the latest sales gimmicks of Barclays Bank and J.P.S. cigarettes.

A train rumbles and clickety-clacks overhead, on its way to Birmingham.

(II)

Granny pushed open the swing doors and let her nine-year-old grand-daughter walk through. She paused for a minute to glance at glossy leaflets about concerts and stately homes on show in the information centre, then pressed the button for one of the lifts up to the new city library.

Once up, having narrowly missed being crushed by the doors closing quicker than she had anticipated, the old lady pottered over to the return counter. She handed over the three books her grandchild had read, then lead her into the children's corner. A crowd of little ones were busy with their pleasure, concentrating hard on choice, pouring over "The Wild Ones" or "Dr Seuss", as they sat on their little red plastic seats, acting very grown-up. Others dashed excitedly to tell brothers about a book on Captain Cook or the railways that they'd discovered, whilst a ten-year-old sat at a table engrossed in "Asterix and The Big Fight".

The young girl wanted a story book about mountaineers, but granny thought "The Princess and The Pea" much more suitable.

"I read that when I was five," she remonstrated.

"It's a lovely story though, Leanne."

"I hate it."

"Are you sure? I'm sure I don't know."

In the end, they take both and wander off to the check-out.

(III)

A young couple carrying Leon Allan and C&A plastic bags stop outside Pizzaland to look at the menu. For them, both in work and without children, they don't really bother about the prices, though they know it isn't an expensive restaurant. They decide on a meal together that evening, to celebrate six months of marriage.

Across the pedestrianised way, the Methodist Central Hall has a placard announcing a bazaar to raise money for Children in Need. Inside the large brick building, the downstairs hall is alive with hundreds of people cramming to buy home-made jams, cakes and pickles, or to have a go on the "Find The Treasure" board, or at "Pick A Straw – And Win A Prize", where every raffle ticket ending in a five wins a grocery item. Others sit at a make-shift café stall, as middle-aged ladies sort through quality second-hand cardigans and baby clothes for new grand-children, think about buying a cruette set or purchasing a framed picture on the White Elephant stall.

Outside, two children play hop and skip on the steps of the hall in their bright new summer dresses.

The 'Coventry Telegraph' building

IT'S A DOG'S LIFE

Charlie the mongrel was kicked out by his old man as usual at seven, when he went off to work. Not for him the luxury of a day in the warm, nor even in a large garden, which his owner, living in an upstairs flat, didn't have.

So he hung around for an hour in the doorway, waiting for the postman, which provided ten minutes entertainment as he followed him along the street, barking.

Last week had been fun. He had followed a bitch on heat and sat outside the house, every day, together with half-a-dozen strays.

About nine, when the shops started to open, he would set off on his rounds, marking his patch and sniffing out potential food, mates and enemies. Today was no exception.

He trotted along Lower Ford Street, an inner city road leading out to the main Leicester road. The workmen drilling and digging a new by-pass were well into it by now. He avoided their stares and carefully skirted their shovels.

The day was warming up as he approached Gosford Road. It was an old shopping street, very busy with cars, dirty and dusty in this summer heat. The new by-pass was intended to solve the problem.

His first sprainting point was the corner of the shop owned by the Cats' Protection League. He raised his snout up to the door, sniffed, and glanced at the display window of secondhand items and clothing. Padding off, nose to the ground, he passed a closed secondhand gas cooker shop, and entered Gosford Street, pausing for a quick sniff and tinkle at the first lamppost. The next shop was being refitted so he hurried past the smell of paint, but stopped to appreciate the scents from the newsagent's and to leave his mark on the drainpipe of the next shop, which was boarded up.

He glanced at the chip-shop across the traffic-filled road. It was closed at the moment, but at lunchtime he would make sure he was there, ready for any spilt chips or fish. The best place, however, was a bin a hundred yards up the hill, where the half-finished packets were thrown.

He dawdled past the secondhand applicances shop and paused to hitch his leg at the corner of the new computer showroom. He had no respect for bright, sparkling paint. In fact the newer, the fewer other dogs' smells, the more satisfying a halt could be.

Past Rembrandt clothes shop at a trot, then a pause to mooch around the door of "The Golden Cup" and the old bric-a-brac outside another secondhand shop. Then a sniff at a passing female doberman on a tight lead, pulled sharply away as he approached.

"What a cheek," he thought, then pottered off again. Past the pet shop – lovely smells of doggie biscuits – and the secondhand book shop, past the shoe repairers and onto a small grass park with a few trees. He met another mongrel there, but a male and he kept his distance, peeing against a few trees, checking out the more recent odours and stopping for a while to tear open a black binbag with some old spare ribs in.

After lying down and crunching the bones for a good hour and growling his fiercest growl at another couple of strays, he stretched and dozed for a while in the shade of a lime tree.

It was early afternoon now. The traffic was thunderous and the smell of diesel and dust was awful. He sensed it was chip-shop time and rose, stretched and sauntered off up the hill towards the bin. Past the dry-cleaners, hairdressers, another newsagent's and Cobwebs, a secondhand shop, past the boarded up Harold Freeman's, Belinda Gowns, and Second Image's nearly new clothes. He paused for a sprinkle at the Video Shop, then scampered past the electrical shop where once he had received a boot in the ribs, past the "Hand in Heart" and "Hertford Arms" on the other side of the street, past the "Pitt's Head" and on. He now had to cross, so waited at the pelican crossing for an old lady to press the button for him and trotted across when he heard the bleeps. He halted by the curry take-away, but it was closed, then peered into a café as he hurried past. Just down a side entry leading to the tattooist, he smelt some chips and shuffled over to the cast-away package. He used his nose to open the screwed up ball and scratched at the remains, before the owner of the café came out and chased him off.

He found a few more chips packets, but nothing great. A poor day. He was at the top of the shopping street now, by the Refuge Lending Society, the Credit Union, Oliver's gold and silver shop and several cheap furniture and clothes shops. He scuttled across the road by the lights, past the JCBs and pneumatic drills working on the top end of the by-pass and into Gosford Park, to while away the afternoon lying on the grass in the shade, watching all those silly humans scurrying about, trying to earn their own scraps.

THE BUCK STOPS HERE

P.C. Gerald Lawrence pulled up by the Cheylesmore shops and turned off the engine of his Metro. He waited.

A local shop-keeper had complained about kids riding bikes along the pavement and knocking an old lady over. He saw a couple of lads on bikes and called them over.

'You know you're not supposed to ride your bikes on the pavement, don't you,' he said. There was no reply. 'Did you knock an old lady down along here?'

'No.'

'Not us.'

'No, sir, to you,' the constable said.

'Yes, sir.'

'Do you know who did?'

'No, sir.'

'Well, don't let me catch you riding along the pavement again, do you hear?'

'Yes, sir.' They turned to go, wheeling their BMXs, but, when safely away, one of the nine-year-olds stuck out his tongue and made a V-sign at him.

'Typical,' Gerald thought. 'There's no respect for a uniform anymore.' There was little else he could do. He had several more calls that morning and had to pop into the shop-keeper as well, to get some details and tell him he had seen the kids.

He pulled out, drove along the slip road by the parade, then parked by the shop which had complained. He got out, entered the shop and had a chat with the very irate man, upset because it had happened numerous times without anyone ever doing anything about it.

It was becoming increasingly frustrating being a police officer. He loved the job. All his life he had wanted nothing else. He loved it because he liked people, had a high social conscience and felt there could be nothing more rewarding in life than serving the community. But he had never realised the intense pressures there would be on him. It was literally going from call to call without stop some days, with no time to get to know the area or members of the community.

He had always felt that patrol cars were not as good as men on the

226

beat. They had been a disaster in fact, cutting the police off from the people. But what else could they do? In 1947, 465 officers dealt with 4,000 crimes. Last year, 585 officers had to deal with 36,000 crimes and 103,000 other incidents. They couldn't go on like that. It was horrific.

He was on his way to a woman who had phoned up at 2 a.m. last night, complaining that her estranged husband had broken in and, after trying to rape her, had beaten her up. A colleague had called last night, but he had to do a follow-up call and get a statement, as last night she had been in a state of shock.

He drove out of the slip road, through the junction and up along Quinton Park, past the pool, the low-rise council blocks and the Cheylesmore Social Club. This part of Cheylesmore was a large council estate, with houses and small blocks of well-built flats, many of them sheltered. He drove along Black Prince Avenue and into Arundel Road.

He was from Birmingham originally, had joined the West Midlands police and been transferred to Coventry last year. He was still getting used to the area. It seemed a pity to him that local bobbies who had grown up near the area they patrolled, weren't used, though with attacks on policemen's houses, he could see why some policemen were reluctant about it.

Take this family dispute. There had been an enormous increase in violence in the home, nearly all towards women. Sometimes they would be beaten up every week, having lived with it for years, until they couldn't cope anymore. But even when they left home, or took a court injunction out on the man, he often still harassed her and made her life a misery.

He drew up, climbed out and knocked on the door. A young woman answered, holding a baby. One of her eyes had a large black and red bruise around it and her lip was cut. She let him in.

He sat and talked, then took her statement. He asked her if she would take her husband to court, but she refused. She was plainly terrified of him doing her in properly if she did that. She knew he would probably only get a suspended sentence, so would be after her again. She seemed totally depressed, petrified of him, but unable to do anything about it.

As he sat there, his radio went and he was called to a house-breaking on Arnold Avenue. He quickly finished the statement and took his leave. He knew it would probably merely be filed, as she wouldn't take any action. So much of his job seemed like a waste of time. Filling in reports, doing paper-work, when he should be preventing crime.

He sat back in his car and drove off, up to The Chesils and into the private estate, with its rows of semis, each with a pleasant, large garden. Policing was being in the front line of society. Governments passed laws, but he had to implement them. He was dealing with the reality.

He had been thrown through a chipshop window once, had alsations set on him, had a brick thrown through his windscreen and he had even had his truncheon ripped from him and used against him. Worst of all, he had been in riot gear on the streets of Handsworth, parrying bricks and petrol bombs.

In general, there was much less authority for uniforms, whether bus inspectors, postmen or the police. Kids were much cheekier, more street-wise, he supposed. It seemed that the schools, the homes, the media all failed to encourage respect for authority.

Unemployment itself wasn't directly responsible for the rise in crime. The unemployed weren't criminal. The real growth was in the 10 to 17 year olds, the juveniles, and it had to be a reflection of the way society was bringing them up. Perhaps it was their expectations as well, he didn't know. All he knew was he was at the thick end of it.

'I think it's the breakdown of society,' he mumbled to himself. His radio was still talking away. A post office in Holbrooks had been raided and there was a car chase going on. He turned up Watercall Avenue and into Arnold Avenue. It was a peaceful, pleasant side of the city, a world away from the poorer areas. The only time they ever met was when there was a crime. One part of the city feared and knew little about the other. It was so noticeable, the city's north/south divide.

"The family isn't respected any more," he thought. "One in five children are born out of wedlock. One in five! Then all the divorce and the lack of discipline in the family. Some parents aren't fulfilling their role at all, there're arguments and drinking, so the children've no idea of purpose in life. Parents don't respect teachers, teachers don't respect authority. Some parents actually accept a degree of criminality, calling it 'pranks' or saying 'Oh, he gets up to all sorts of things' and laughing it off. Punishment isn't a deterrent for kids any more. They need deterrents all the way through life. They should be taught what was right and wrong all the time. Discipline and respect had to start in the family and within the home. The main deterrent for most people isn't the law or the threat of prison, it's their own inate sense of what's right and wrong, of their own moral boundaries, of how they should behave as decent human

228

beings. That was the moral basis of society, more than the law. But that was being broken down now."

He pulled up and went along the path, ducking under the branches of a cherry tree, past the beautifully trim lawn and flowering rose bushes and rang the bell on the double-glazed front porch door.

The inside of the house was a tip. The woman was very upset. Her husband, who had just hurried away from work, was there, carefully itemising the losses, not disturbing anything.

Gerald sat and took notes for his report. He promised a finger-print man and checked the mode of entry – an unlocked kitchen door. A simple mistake and a home ruined.

The woman was nearly hysterical, whilst her husband tried to stay calm and wanted to know what the police would do. He promised to take statements from the neighbours as well. Everyone needed and deserved so much time, yet there was so little to spare. He secretly knew that the chances of catching the thief were remote unless he had committed a serious blunder, but he would check out a few likely perpetrators and get C.I.D. onto it.

He still had a reported mugging of an elderly woman to deal with and a reported stolen car, but wanted his lunch-break, so headed back to the police station. He would have a lot of paper-work to do there as well.

Things were getting so out of proportion. There was the looney left and the rabid right, there was more robbery on the streets, more stupid, vile activities, like peeing in letterboxes or ripping out telephones, which seemed so senseless and pathetic he didn't understand it at all.

He hadn't joined the police force to don riot gear. He didn't want to guard demos, struggle with mass pickets, break up football hooligans, intervene in gang fights, or have abuse hurled at him for being a fascist or being soft on the Trots.

It wasn't how he had imagined the job, that was for sure. People said they never ever saw a policeman, that they had lost touch with them. The personal touch, with an ear to the ground, knowing everything that went on, had been replaced by a quick crime report, then off again, running ragged from call to call. He wasn't surprised the public had lost a lot of their faith in the police and felt the police weren't interested in their problems.

The police were the last resort. When everything else failed, call in a copper and let him sort out the mess, whether a pub brawl, a family bust-up, a juvenile caught for thieving, or a young prostitute on heroin. If it wasn't solved, it was all the policeman's fault. They never considered the years of decline of that person, the environment he had grown up in, the pressures, the problems, the way life had treated him. No, it was all the poor copper's fault. He was society's final safety-net when all else had failed.

He drove along the Leamington Road, past the spacious, tree-filled Memorial Park, past the railway station and onto the inner ring-road.

Social deprivation was a big thing. Lack of money put big pressures on families. There was nothing worse. It led to stress, discontent, dissatisfaction, bitterness and came out in the kids.

He turned off the ring-road, past the Cheylesmore Employment Benefit Office, into Little Park Street and carefully turned into the police car park.

Norms had changed so much. Today's norm had been abhorrent ten years ago. People thought so little of murders and rapes now. Nothing shocked them. They accepted it happened. We had lost our intolerance and sense of humanity. The police could never expect a member of the public to automatically help them out now, especially in areas where there was bitterness by some towards the police and where they were as likely to turn against you. The middle-of-the-road majority moaned a lot, but wouldn't come forward to help. They tended to shut their doors on what was happening, safe within their castles. But now more of their castles were being invaded. That was devastating for them. The victims were often traumatised, totally devastated by it. Everyone was effected these days.

As he parked his car and locked it, he remembered the policemen's ball on soon. There was a rehearsal that evening. He was playing a fairy godmother. It was a kids' panto to raise funds for some local charities. It was the side of policework people rarely saw and yet it was a side which meant as much to him.

230

THE OLD-TIME DANCE HALL

May and Charles paid their entrance fee and greeted their old friends. Already, the hall of the A.E.U. building was nearly full with people sitting around the tables and along the walls.

On the stage, the "Nostalgics", a three-piece band of piano, sax and drums, was harmonising to a thirties' arrangement whilst a dozen couples danced across the floor.

'Hello there, May.'

'Hello, Francis darling. How are you? Hi there, Bert.'

'Hello, May. Hello Charles.'

The newly arrived couple sat by their friends. The band had just changed to an old, familiar song.

> *'I'm singing in the rain*
> *Just singing in the rain,*
> *What a glorious feeling,*
> *I'm happy again . . .'*

'I haven't seen you for weeks, Francis. How's the St Christopher's Church Group going?'

'Oh, we're visiting about a hundred old people now. We've just had another summer outing. That's why I've not been here. I've had all the planning to do.'

> *'I'm laughing at clouds,*
> *So dark up above,*
> *The sun's in my heart*
> *And I'm ready for love . . .'*

'There's a lot here today,' Bert said.

'A few more fellas than usual, too,' Charles added.

> *'With a happy refrain,*
> *Just singing, singing in the rain.'*

The singer did a little tap-dance and a twirl, as he went 'da-da-da-da' down the microphone, ending amongst a lively round of applause and

231

cheers.

The Friday afternoon old-time music hall had been going on for a long time now and was very popular. Francis was active in one of the many Age Concern groups covering the city. Mostly, they did visiting, but they also organised trips, luncheon clubs and fund-raising events. It could be tiring at times, but was extremely rewarding.

The "Nostalgics" changed the atmosphere with an old crooner's song, bringing back the memories as the couples stared into each others eyes and smiled.

> 'Blue Moon, you saw me standing alone,
> Without a dream in my heart,
> Without a love of my own . . .'

Age Concern ran a workshop in Earlsdon and held regular campaigns both to spot-light the plight of the old and amongst the elderly themselves, to encourage them to keep warm or save on their electricity. They had several day centres run in conjunction with Social Services and the Health Authority, ran exhibitions in the city centre and spoke at meetings.

> 'And then there suddenly appeared before me,
> The only one my arms could ever hold,
> I heard you whisper "Please adore me,"
> And when I looked, the moon had turned to gold . . .'

The winter was always terrible for the old. She had known an old woman who had died from hyperthermia, frightened to turn on the heating because of the bills. Many of the elderly were housebound, isolated and frail. There was a lot of loneliness behind those bolted doors.

> 'Blue Moon, now I'm no longer alone,
> Without a dream in my heart,
> Without a love of my own . . .'

'Come on Charlie, let's dance,' said May, bullying her reluctant husband.

'Oh,' he moaned.

'Come on, or you won't get your tea tonight.'

'Oh,' he repeated. 'So long as the next one's a waltz.'

Unfortunately for him, it was.

IN THE CO-OP

Mary was sixty-seven on Sunday, so had decided to treat herself to a little extra that week. She had gone to her local butcher's and bought a tenderised steak, the first steak she'd had since her Bill had died last January in the cold spell. It had been a bit more than she had expected, but it would be worth it.

She entered the Co-op, having to use all her strength to push the stiff swing doors, through the revolving barrier of the food hall and pulled at a trolley, until it eventually jerked free of the rest in the rack. It was just what she needed, a tug-of-war with metal monsters on a Monday morning. As usual, the trolley had a will of its own and those stupid, anarchistic wheels each seemed to want to go its own way. She grappled with the drunken crate as she pushed it down the aisle, hitting a pillar and nearly coming to grief in the jams.

She wanted some oxtail soup, so tried to turn it, attempting to get the right angle for the lurch across to the other side of the aisle. Heinz were always a few pence more expensive, so she decided on a tin of the Co-op brand. Half tins were only a little cheaper and, always with an eye for value, she knew a larger can would do her for two meals. Next, a pot of marmalade, again the Co-op label, then some tinned fruit. She checked each type of fruit for price. Pears were 33p, fruit cocktail 35p and peaches 32p. She really fancied some pineapple slices, but they were on the top shelf and, as she was only five foot one tall, they were out of reach. She looked around. A young man was just behind her.

'Could you get me a tin of pineapple please,' she asked him.

'Sure.' He reached up. 'Slices?'

'Yes please.'

'Here you are then, my darling.'

She was dismayed when she saw the price, but kept quiet. She daren't leave it, now she'd asked. Oh, but she couldn't afford that. She put it in her trolley, deciding to put it back on another shelf. She also put a tin of peaches in the trolley. Then, perilously on, her muscles struggling to keep the wire beast going in a vaguely straight line. Some Red Label margarine, a packet of shortcake biscuits, a small brown loaf, then along the next aisle, picking some toilet rolls and surreptitiously depositing the pineapple with the toothpastes. So many brands, so many gimmicks, so many additives, so much advertising and pretty packaging, all to get you to buy toothpaste. Surely, she thought, toothpaste was toothpaste.

Next, a small piece of Cheshire cheese from the cold bay. Then a packet of rice crispies, and some frozen peas. Then a wait in the queue at the cold meat counter. She couldn't eat firm meat, because of her dentures, but loved gently chewing some ham or haslet. It was a change from liver. She took two onions and two pounds of potatoes at the vegetable counter and then made her way to the checkout.

As she was struggling over there with the obstreperous tin tyrant, she suddenly remembered she only had four pounds on her. Her heart started to race and she began to sweat. She was sure she had more than four pounds worth of things here.

"Oh, heavens," she thought, "I can't bear it if I have to put things back at the checkout. It's so awful." She remembered the biscuits. They could be the first to go. She pushed to the bread section and slipped them in amongst the thick sliced. She was sure she still had too much. She started to count the things up, bending painfully into the trolley. "Why," she thought, "are these things always made for six-foot weight trainers?" She added up. Rice crispies, 99 pence. Soup 27 pence, that's 1 pound, 26pence. Toilet rolls, 1 pound, 92 pence. Cheese, 2 pounds, 68 pence. Marg., 2 pounds, 96 pence. Ham, 3 pounds, 9 pence. Haslet, 3 pounds, 68 pence. Potatoes, . . ." she couldn't see the price clearly. "Ah, nine pence, that's 3 pounds, er . . . 3 pounds, 77 pence."

The onions were 10 pence, bread 36 pence for a small loaf, and the frozen peas 56 pence. The total came to 4 pounds 79 pence.

She felt the tears of humiliation welling inside her. What could she put back? It couldn't be the cold meats or the vegetables, not after she'd specially asked for them. And she'd set her heart on the peaches and peas for her birthday meal. What was inessential? What was a luxury? She felt it was life itself she couldn't afford.

It would have to be the toilet rolls. She had half a roll left. It would last the weekend. And the margarine. And the milkman would just have to be patient this Friday.

She put the toilet rolls and margarine back as innoccuously as she could amongst the biscuits and then pushed and pulled the obstructionist carry-all back towards the checkout. The woman whisked it all through and helped her to pack it all into her canvas shopping bag and a plastic carrier she had brought with her. It was a Sainsburys' one, but who cared? Then she hobbled out, carrying her few items towards the bus stop and home.

THE AGE CONCERN WORKSHOP

Ernie picked up the old chair frame and turned it from side to side, inspecting it and assessing how best to re-fit the seat.

It was old, with spring and horsehair padding. He had already webbed it up and hand-sewn the springs into the hessian, top and bottom, covered it with a layer of horsehair and lain another layer of hessian on that. Now he was finishing the second row of stitching around the frame to give the seat a good edge, tightly sewed, and to stop the seat falling away.

These seats weren't like the modern ones. Those just had foam covered with hessian and an outer cover of plastic or dralon. It was only the hessian holding you up, plus, sometimes, some zig-zag springs, stretch springs, or rubber webbing. That foam was a fire hazard as well and disintegrated after a while.

He knotted off the thread and inspected the seat, checking it was done properly and neatly. Putting it down, he went over to a box and sorted through some decron and wool, before selecting some for the padding. The outer covering was going to be a deep burgundy leather. He had put that to one side a few days ago. It was part of a batch of off-cuts from the Jag, where he had worked most of his life.

For twenty-three years, he had been a coach trimmer at the Brown's Lane plant, then had spent four years as a training instructor. He was now retired and worked in this craftshop for Age Concern. Elderly people in need of a cheap repair service could bring in their furniture and have it put right, as long as they supplied their own material.

He had come to Coventry in 1958, after spending the War doing coach trimming work on army trucks and ambulances and many years in Leeds building buses.

He fitted the seat into the chair frame and placed the leather on top, arranging it for the best fit.

Retirement had brought him a whole new life. He'd made more friends than he ever had at work. There'd been no time then. Workmates were just acquaintances. He enjoyed this work a lot more as well. There it had been very repetitive, but here every day was different. He made pram aprons, chairs, even rocking horses.

He looked around the large room. In the middle was a kiln for the pottery class. There were woodwork benches and vices. On the shelves and tables, around the walls, there were pots, a doll's house, a kiddies' garage, stools, dolls, and much more. There was an industrial sewing machine and, inside the door of a locker, Ernie's array of upholstery tools. The centre was building up its own set of equipment gradually and the rest were loans from helpers who worked there. The Jag gave them veneers and leather off-cuts and Burbages let them have some wood. Occasionally, people would leave a small donation to the centre in their wills.

He stretched the leather to the back rest, cut it at an angle in one corner by the back upright, turned it in, stretched it around the upright and started tacking it around the edge. He picked up the tacks and put each one in his sealed lips, then used his magnetic tack hammer to take it from his mouth and bang it through the leather and into the wood.

It had been hard work at the Jag. It hadn't been the management who had turned its fortunes round, but the workforce. Workers had spent their whole lives in that firm.

He had seen a lot of changes there. It was all compressed air now. He remembered the stuffing iron he had used to push the horsehair into the seat. They had employed tufting needles, about a foot long, to button the seats with jute string and circular frenching needles to sew up the backs. Now it was nylon and synthetic materials like ambla instead of leather and buttons had gone as moulded seats had come in. But, in many ways they were better seats. The nylon didn't rot and synthetic materials stretched more and didn't scratch as easily. Before the War, all cars had hide, but it was too expensive now, at three or four pounds a square foot. However, with foam there was nothing to take the shock of a person's weight, whereas the old upholstery lasted for years.

At one time, they had done everything at Brown's Lane, but now the bodies came in from Castle Bromwich and the engines and axles from Radford. Brown's Lane was just final assembly and trim.

He tacked along the back rest to the other back upright and stretched the leather around it, as he had done with the first. Then, still stretching it, he tacked up the side.

At the Jag, they had leather cutters for the hides. It was a skilled job, cutting a hide, because none were without holes or blemishes. He had to stick the foam on the seat and machine it up, then bench-trim it. There used to be a lot of tacking, but now it was all glueing and foam. It was less work, but those solvents were deadly. Although there were large extractor fans, you could get high on them and had to watch for sparks, because of the flammable vapours.

He put another tack in his lips. Around the table were odds and ends. A stapler, some glue brushes, a couple of chisels and a screwdriver, a few springs, a pair of scissors and a cardboard box with pieces of foam in.

He tacked up the last side, stretching it over the corner, and pushing in the wool stuffing to make the rounded shape. Then he took out a sharp knife and trimmed the edge straight. Putting the chair down, he opened a box of braiding bobbins and selected some in red. Getting his glue, he carefully brushed it over the edge of the leather and the tacks.

Jocelyn popped her bright head in. She was on a Community Programme job for a year.

"The trouble was", Ernie confided to himself, "you just got used to her and the year was over." She told him another customer had arrived and he told her he would be out in a minute. She stopped for a short while to admire the new seat, then left again.

With the glue on, Ernie carefully stuck down the braiding around the edge, cut it and stuck down the end. All finished, he stood the chair upright on his table to admire his handiwork, wiped the glue from his hands and went off to meet the new customer.

The Coventry Over 60s Bowling Club

THE HOME HELP

Marjorie pulled another frond of Iris's wet hair between her fingers, wrapped it over the curler, then rolled it in towards her scalp and clipped it down.

'Did you go to the day centre yesterday?' the home help asked the elderly woman.

Iris didn't hear her.

'Iris,' Majorie spoke louder and closer to her ear, 'did the ambulance pick you up yesterday?'

'Oh yes, yes.'

'What was the meal like?'

'There weren't many potatoes and the gravy was cold.'

'Oh dear.'

'There were only three tiny potatoes.'

'Oh dear. Was Mrs Watson there?'

'Pardon?'

'Mrs Watson?'

'Oh, yes, yes.' Iris paused. 'The ambulance driver was that awful young man.'

'Uh huh.'

'He's got rough hands. He's always in such a hurry, not like the other one.'

'Oh dear.' Marjorie chatted away, as she clipped the curlers around Iris's head. Iris had been on her own for eight years and the loneliness was getting to her. It was sad to see her gradual deterioration. Her disorientation had become much worse the last week or two and she had started mumbling to herself. Now, nothing was good enough for her and she would complain whatever happened.

'Would you like a cup of tea, Iris?'

'Oh yes.'

'I'll get you one then.' She put in the last curler.

Iris sat in her chair whilst Marjorie went into the kitchen. She didn't move because, without Marjorie to help, she would fall. She had broken her leg that way last year. She had recently gone on the waiting list for an old people's home and would soon be moving into one.

Marjorie laid out a plate of biscuits for Iris on the kitchen table. In the evening, another home help would come to cook her a light meal and help her change for bed. She would get Iris some Horlicks and a biscuit and, some evenings, help Iris have a bath, write a letter for her, or cut and varnish her nails.

Being a home help was like that. It wasn't being a general dogsbody or house-cleaner, although it was important to keep the house tidy. It was to give Iris the personal care she needed, to be with her and talk to her, give her some mental stimulation and make sure she was alright.

Marjorie had been trained to cope with most contingencies. She could do basic medical tasks, such as giving medication or changing simple dressings, though injections and changing catheters she left to the district nurse. She knew about the ageing process, that many elderly found it difficult to come to terms with. Iris had still tried to do all the dusting in the house and fallen off a chair, breaking her leg. She had been a battler against ageing for years, but had noticably given up in the last month. She couldn't climb her stairs now. Nor could she look up, as her neck had grown stiff.

Marjorie looked after three elderly women. She visited Wilma on Tuesday mornings, a lovely woman, but with terrible arthritis. Marjorie did what she could to keep her house tidy, mainly the heavy jobs like vacuuming and a bit of ironing. Wilma had a very caring daughter who visited several times a week and was also picked up by the ambulance every day to go to the day centre.

She also called on Betty twice a week. She was chair-bound, but a bright spark and Marjorie made her bed, did her washing, vacuumed, and watered the plants.

With each of them, the most important part of the work was to mentally stimulate and motivate them. She tried to be positive and cheerful. Iris had given up and become very resentful. She had lost all her fun and laughter and the colour had gone out of her cheeks. Marjorie kept telling her to get the best out of the years she had left, to do things, even if it was merely to read the paper which Marjorie brought into the livingroom-cum-bedroom each morning, but it wasn't working any more.

Marjorie poured the tea into the cups, added milk and sugar and gave them a stir. She picked up the biscuits and carried them in, putting them on a coffee table near Iris. The woman was staring forward. Marjorie went out again and brought back the two cups of tea.

'Are you going to do my hair today?' Iris asked.

'Yes Iris, I've done it for you.'

'You have? I don't remember. It was terrible last week. I don't want it if you can't do it properly. I didn't go out at all, I was so ashamed.'

'It will be nice this time.'

'You always forget something. It's never right.'

'Is the nurse coming tomorrow?'

'It's never right.'

'I think she's coming to check your blood pressure and see about your arm.'

'They only want to take me away. Last time they wanted to put me in the workhouse.'

'We don't have them any more.'

'She said so.'

'She's just going to check you're alright Iris.'

Each morning, Marjorie helped Iris get up, get washed and dressed and gave her her breakfast. She then stayed on to talk and do other necessary tasks for an hour until the ambulance arrived to take her to the day centre. Tomorrow, when the nurse came, she would tell her how much Iris had deteriorated.

In the evenings, after making her tea and getting her changed, Marjorie helped Iris into bed, put out the milk bottle, tidied up and locked the backdoor. She was like a child in many ways and had to be cared for accordingly. She was growing more mentally infirm day by day. Her memory was going, which was why Marjorie would ask her what she had done the day before, just to stimulate it and keep it working. Iris would often forget basic things like where she had put her glasses a few moments before, or forget to eat her lunch.

'I see Coventry City have reached Wembley, Iris. That's exciting, isn't it. D'you thing they'll win?'

'Who?'

'Coventry City. The football.'

'Oh yes.' Iris's eyes suddenly sparkled. 'George followed them for years. I wish he was here now to see it. It's marvellous. I used to go myself, years ago, but not now of course.'

As quickly as it had come the smile went and the moment was lost.

Iris, Wilma and Betty all lived in Holbrooks, Betty in a well-built council house, the others in private property. Iris lived on Beake Avenue, the main road through that part of the city. It was wide with houses lining it which became more modern, with larger gardens, the further you went up it. She lived opposite the church of the Holy Family which she had been to all her life, with its infant school alongside where two of her grandchildren were now attending.

It was a pleasant area. The neighbours were considerate, there were good shops nearby and the buses ran right outside. When she had been more mobile, Iris had often caught the bus to the Radford shopping centre and called into the post office there to cash her pension book.

Marjorie rose to make the bed. She had to hurry as the ambulance would be there soon.

Iris had a daughter who lived nearby. She was very caring, but worked as a teacher, so couldn't call during the week. The strain on her had been enormous as well.

For some families who had an elderly person living with them the pressures could be dreadful. It was like having a child around the house, but a mobile and often aggressive one. It could drive them up the wall. And, as usual, it was the mothers in the families, the carers, who usually carried the extra burden.

Marjorie worried about those families. Coping with an elderly person could be very wearing. Watching them gradually change and worsen was often shattering. Death sometimes came as a relief to the elderly. Many spent their last years in pain and were upset at not being able to do the shopping and housework and at being incontinent or in bed all day. The families often felt a tremendous burden lifted from their shoulders as well. That feeling of relief at death, of feeling glad when they ought to feel grief, created a lot of guilt in many people. They sometimes had to be counselled, told that their feelings were natural and encouraged to be positive about the sacrifice they had made for the grand-parent over the years.

A woman may feel guilty at the resentment she has had for a long time towards the old person for imposing herself upon the family, anger at the sense of powerlessness to do anything about her situation and frustration at other members of the family refusing to help out. She may never have articulated this resentment at the conflict and at having her own life ruined.

Marjorie checked Iris's hair. It had nearly dried. She went to the cupboard, took out the hairdryer and plugged it in, then blew warm air carefully over the frail white hair. She knew of an association for carers in Coventry, which gave families support and advice and discussed with them the needs of the elderly, where stress may lay and what the problems were. It offered counselling to the carers and explained the role of social services to relieve them by supplying home helps or taking the elderly to day centres.

As Marjorie started to unclip the curlers and gently unwind them, letting the hair spring back into rolls and, with a soft brush and the dryer, brushing it out a bit for her, Iris started to mumble about her daughter. Marjorie asked about her and chatted generally about her news.

Some carers became so fraught that they had nervous breakdowns themselves. They might even feel like throttling the old person or walking out. Caring for an elderly person could be similar, in one way, to having an unemployed man about. The house was suddenly not your own, you were living on top of one another and you couldn't relax. You felt you had lost control over your life. Your doctor prescribes you sedatives and anti-depressants, but nothing really helps.

Not all people in need of home helps were elderly. Some young mothers, who perhaps had been in care themselves, found it impossible to cope. Here, the role of the home help or family aide, as they were called, was not to do things for the parent so much as *with* her, showing her how to change a nappy, make a bottle, or deal with piles of washing. The problem may be how to budget on social security or how to keep the kids clean at school. Deserted mothers left with three or four children may be totally demoralised and have let things go downhill, with little money and all the high bills still coming in which, a few months ago, there was plenty of money to pay for. The kids too may, in their own way, be grieving. They may be slower at school, start bed-wetting, or get into fights. Nor was it true that people abused the state benefits system. Often they didn't even know their basic rights. So the family aide built the mother's morale, helped her with the children and talked things over with her, tiding her over her inability to cope or her sense of inadequacy at losing her husband and helping her stop taking it out on the children, if she had been.

The policy of closing hospitals and emptying the mental wards was not well thought out. The institutionalised were suddenly having to cope without sufficient back-up because other services were so overstretched. They floundered and despaired, often not knowing how to pay the bills, or to use a launderette, or even to queue at the post office. There was a need for more residential homes, halfway houses and shelterd flats, where people could gradually pick up the reins of living independently, yet have a warden nearby should they get into any bother.

A day out in Broad Gate

Otherwise, for some of the mentally ill it could become a vicious circle of being left on their own, of getting into debt, drinking, of being taken back to hospital, then released again for more of the same. So home helps would attempt to give a pattern to these people's lives, talk to them about eating and dressing properly, encourage them to meet friends, help them write letters, or talk over their problems with them. Often, for these forgotten people, everyday life was so stressful it led to self-neglect, worry and anxiety, with its attendant nervous ailments and illnesses.

Marjorie put the hair dryer away and glanced at her watch.

'Come on Iris, shall we get your coat on? The ambulance will be here soon.'

'I hope it's that other man with the tie. I didn't like the young one at all. He was too much in a hurry.'

Marjorie helped her up and put on her coat. As she was doing so, she heard the ambulance pull up outside. She fetched Iris's shoes and her handbag and then helped her outside. It was the man with the tie, so Iris cheered up again.

The elderly were living longer now. There had been a big rise in the over seventy-fives and, what with the advances in medicine such as heart pacemakers, frailer people were living longer as well. That was increasing the work-load on everybody, on the district nurses, social workers, home helps and those churches which were major carers of the elderly with no families.

Unemployment and the rise in the number of broken families also added to the stress on people and the number dependent on social services. The extended family had declined and the caring generation was getting progressively older. There were, though, more men involved in voluntary work these days. They were good for the elderly men, to help motivate them and talk about "malish" things.

Marjorie helped the driver lift Iris into the twelve-seater white minibus. Being a home help was a physical job as well, up and down stairs, lifting people into baths, doing the shopping or commoding.

She waved goodbye as the ambulance pulled away, then went back inside to clear away the tea cups and lock up.

She felt a great deal of satisfaction in her job. She was very interested in people and enjoyed using her own initiative. She had responsibility and trust, though at times, being alone with a person who might suddenly collapse, have a fit, or be in a bad mood, could be frightening.

There were also occasions when she took the job home with her, but as she had two teenage sons of her own, she had no time for too much reflection.

If a person she cared for went into hospital, Marjorie felt it was only right to visit her and remember her birthday. The elderly might be difficult at times, but many were lively and full of fun. For some, their worlds had narrowed considerably and worries were blown out of proportion. They might never be happy or grateful, but run the whole gamut of emotions. Sometimes she could do nothing right.

Marjorie put on her coat, checked that the lights and cooker were off, then pulled the front door to. Above all, she had to be adaptable and sensitive. She had to be aware of people's pride and dignity, allow space for grief if necessary, or give them support if needed. Often a couple were like two old gates, propping each other up. If one went, the other would just give up. There was often fear amongst the old as well, fear of vandalism and muggings, or of kids who were making a noise. The young seemed threatening, with their strength, to people who had lost all their own power and control of what others did to them and for them. It was easy for them to become cynical and bitter, going over and over things, shaping them the way they wanted them to be. They sometimes saw the young as intolerant, whilst the young, in their turn were scared or ignorant of the elderly. Both sides were vulnerable and therefore defensive.

She turned down Beake Avenue to the bus stop. She looked at her watch. "Good," she thought, "there's one due. I should have just enough time to do my own cleaning and wash my hair."

GO FOR IT CITY!

The team boards its new coach on the Friday before the game, watched by disabled children especially invited to the send-off. As they load the gear, John Sillett waves to them. The cleaning staff at the City ground, dressed in Sky Blue kit, cheer and wave as the players climb aboard. They sing "Go for it City!" as it pulls out. It's going to be that sort of weekend.

Above the entrance to the "Coventry Evening Telegraph" offices is a large picture of John Sillett and George Curtis hugging each other in jubilation on the pitch at Hillsborough, after winning the semi-final. A large placard reads:

"Good Luck Sky Blues, F.A. Cup Finalists, 1987."

Steve Orgrizovic's wife Carolyn has a baby girl. They call her Rachel.

Walking around town, or shopping, people are dressed in sky blue and white, with rosettes, blue teddies, caps and scarves.

Every school in the city has spontaneously decked its class rooms in paintings and montages of the team and the scenes that will take place at Wembley. Lloyds Bank in town has a display of some of them in its foyer, many with the forecast winning goal hitting the back of the net.

A ticket is raffled for Warwick's Myton Hospice, others for Children In Need and two for children with heart disease.

Richards Shops give free outfits to all the players' wives, plus a champagne reception. Another firm has made special blue and white striped suits. Clothes shops report a boom in sales of blue and white dresses and blouses.

Bennett wins the ball on the Leeds goal-line, he crosses hard and low to Gynn, who smashes the ball into the net.

The library had decked itself in scarves and banners. It puts up a display of the match programmes, following City's progress through each round.

245

Touts in town sell banners and scarves on the cheap. A woman walks past covered in rosettes. There are queues for Wembley programmes outside many of the newsagents. The kids are talking about nothing else.

Houchen steals the ball inside the penalty area, beats his man and shoots past Mervyn Day. City 2, Leeds 1!

Every day, the "Evening Telegraph" has pages of articles on the team and on people getting into the mood. The regional T.V. stations run reports every day. The national media starts to arrive in the city.

Owen Owen's has a big placard up saying "Super City" and, down the windows on the other side of the shop, huge posters reading "Go For It City". It's the first time in years a Midlands team has reached Wembley. You can feel that everywhere north of Finchley is gunning for the Sky Blues.

Numerous streets in the city are bedecked in bunting, balloons, posters and banners, bringing the whole community to life. People talk to others they've not spoken to for years. Old niggling differences are forgotten, new friendships are made. Everyone is happy. The city has a totally different atmosphere. For a while, fear is replaced with joy and brotherhood.

A baby clothes shop has all its window display in blue and white, including little babygrows, potties and dresses. Two child models are decked in Sky Blue, with their rosettes and scarves. The Income Tax Office at Parkside has ribbons in the windows and a placard up saying "Good Luck City". Newsagents have displays with photographs of the team, banners, scarves and official match programmes.

Every other car seems to have Sky Blue streamers fluttering from its aerial.

Regis heads the ball down to Houchen. There's a scramble for it in the penalty area. The ball bobs free and Bennett is there to slot it home. Coventry have got to Wembley! Hillsborough erupts!

The banks and building societies all have window displays. The Coventry Building Society has rosettes and cut-out cups in its windows and a big banner outside, reading "Well Done Sky Blues".

In every pub in the city, "Go For It City" is played again and again. People stay behind late to sing and discuss Saturday. The mood is fantastic. We see the odds are all against Coventry, we watch as the pundits back Tottenham, we know about their stars and England players, against the City nobodies, but we all believe, really believe, the City will do it. People even play pool in their City caps and scarves. They probably sleep in them as well.

Late on Friday night, a trickle of cars starts leaving for Wembley. A car with a souped-up engine screeches around Broadgate, flags, streamers and scarves billowing, its horn blasting.

It is Saturday morning. The M.1 is like a carnival procession. The service stations are full of City fans, singing and cheering. The Belgrade Theatre has a sign reading "To All Your Players, From All Of Ours - Good Luck City!"

The De Vere Hotel has the idea of a "no football" weekend. It doesn't get a single booking.

Winnie Lakin, the Lord Mayor, is on her way down, having also been to Hillsborough and joined in the celebrations on the pitch up there.

Brian Burrows twists his knee in the game against Southampton and collapses. He is helped off the pitch by the physio, George Dalton.

Marshall crosses from the goal-line, Steve Livingstone rises and heads home. The youth team have beaten Charlton and won the youth cup! It's a tremendous omen!

Ticket touts offer £25 tickets for £300.

Mercia Sounds blasts out "Go For It." Many of its adverts are from local firms supporting the Sky Blues. They interview John and George live and report from The Compleat Angler, the team's hotel by the Thames.

Pool Meadow bus station is a sea of blue as supporters wait to board their buses. People are waving banners and singing.

Grandstand starts its coverage. Saint and Greavsie are on I.T.V. People at home settle down with cans of beer, sandwiches and snacks. The dogs are put into the kitchen, or allowed to watch if they're quiet.

The Leeds Permanent Building Society has a sign in its window:

"Good Luck Coventry City, from The Leeds. No hard feelings, L.U.F.C."

The queues at the railway station start to extend along the nearby roads, waiting for the special trains.

The fountains in the city are all sky blue.

Along Corporation Street, there are pennants in blue and white, with the city logo of Lady Godiva. Boots has a large window display and is draped in bunting.

Cars and minibuses are now in a flood out of the city, cheered on by crowds along the London Road and Walsgrave Road. Outside Wembley, it is all sky blue, with hardly a Tottenham supporter in sight.

That Friday night, the Co-op offered 10% off all items as a special concession. It has large banners up proclaiming "Congratulations To The Sky Blues."

Mercia Sound reports from the team hotel on score predictions, a wedding across the way, the team coach as it leaves for Wembley, and what the players had for breakfast.

The market starts to close early. It is decked out in ribbons and streamers. The stallholders are wearing blue, with large rosettes, caps and scarves. No-one is going to miss the match.

Mercia News reports that two people had committed suicide. One had put his head on a railway track and been decapitated, the other was a man who was asphixiated in his car, his second attempt in a week.

On the coaches going down, people sing and cheer and drink. The windows are covered with scarves and banners. As they pass cars, they laugh and cheer. People lean out and wave. Happy groups do hokey-cokeys around the service stations.

Annie Oathen is enthusing live from Wembley on the radio, with a reporter interviewing fans along Engineers Way.

Lancaster and Thorpe opticians have a window full of balloons and rosettes, with spectacles and cases in blue.

"Coventree Edukashun Dept Saloot The Sky Bloos."

The players come onto the pitch, to soak up the atmosphere and to satisfy the media with photos and interviews.

Harveys Women's Wear has whole window displays in white and light blue: bras, girdles, nighties, suspenders, blouses, dresses, slips. Babies, with their prams and buggies, are attired in blue, with rosettes and balloons.

The celebrity match on the pitch between the Frostspurs and Sky Blues starts. The final score is 2 - 1 to the team in white. A commentator says of Jimmy Tarbuck, playing for the City: 'Live at the Palladium, knackered at Wembley.' Frost looks tired. 'But,' the commentator asks, 'do you think he should have sunbathed during the match, though?'

Mothercare has a large poster along its window supporting the City, "Win or Loose."

The band plays "Abide with Me."

'Here we go, Here we go, Here we go!' resonates around the stadium.

Shops close as staff turn on portable T.V.s in the backs. The radio commentators on Mercia Sound are already nervous wrecks and the ball hasn't been kicked yet.

Marks and Spencer has a window display, as does British Home

Stores.

On Friday night, Park Lane night club was full of singing, dancing fans, celebrating before the day. It will be their weekend.

A whole family walks around, dressed in blue and white.

Greaves goes for Spurs! We can't lose!

After the Southampton game, the crowds surge onto the pitch. The police use horses to disperse the happy, singing fans. Two disabled children are knocked over.

The team walk onto the pitch. The stadium erupts again. They are presented to the Duchess of Kent, then run off to warm up.

John Thomas has come over from California to be at Wembley. He was an engineer at Rolls Royce and still gets the sports Pink sent out every week.

A couple who married on Friday are honeymooning at Wembley.

Kick off.

A poodle trots along the road with a Sky Blue coat on.

Waddle jinks in on the right, sells Downs a dummy, bangs in a cross and Allen flashes home a header. Inside two minutes, Spurs are ahead. City's normal abysmal start. But it concentrates the mind wonderfully and the players realise they are in a match.

When the tickets were first sold early on Monday, over 4,000 fans who had camped out since Saturday lined up for them. Angry fans complained that they had missed out. Some rushed out of work to join the queue.

Whitley Hospital and Paybody Hospital are closing.

City start attacking, winning the ball in mid-field, Lloyd McGrath marks Hoddle closely, Pickering supports Downs defensively along the left. City's confidence rises as their game plan emerges.

'City! City! City! Here we go! Here we Go!' echoes around. Although Spurs are up, their fans can't match the Coventry end.

Evans Clothes Shop has a window display full of blue and white. Dorothy Perkins has its models in blue. Saxone has a blue and white shoe display.

The tide of the match is turning. Spurs are closed down. The noise from the city end is deafening. The ball is chipped in by Downs, Houchen heads down, Clemence rushes out, Bennett nips in, beats him, and side-foots it into the net. One all! The City end erupts!

Goldie's Gift and Toy Shop is all in blue. Blue balloons, blue streamers, blue teddies, blue dolls, blue Care Bears, blue plates, blue light shades, and a blue clown on a monocycle.

Oxfam has a Sky Blue window display.

"Go For It" stickers are up everywhere.

Bennett crosses from the right, Houchen rises, Regis heads it firmly past Clemence. A second's joy, then dismay as it is disallowed. No-one knows why.

'Coventry's name is on the cup,' Sillett had said. He looks like being right. The crowd starts its "Highfield Wave."

Ogrizovic decides to win it all by himself. He dribbles out of his area and passes straight to Hoddle. The shot is blocked by Peake. A sigh of relief goes up.

W.H.Smiths, Athena, Hudsons, all have window displays. So do Paul Kerry Menswear, Drucker's Patisserie, The Card Shop with its light blue cards, Intershop with its balloons, streamers and ribbons, Cherie Fashions with its models in blue and white, balloons and flags, Co-op Travel with its balloons, Odell Estate Agents with its flags and balloons, Sue Ryder Fashions with its blue and white window display, J.J.B. Sports, with its window full of scarves and light blue sports wear and Sellright with its models in wedding dresses holding banners, wearing rosettes and with sky blue posies.

A free kick for Spurs on their right. Hoddle floats the ball over. Peake misses, Kilcline, harried by Mabbutt, lets it hit his foot. Before he knows it, it has beaten the stranded Orgrizovic and Spurs are back in the lead.

The city centre is deserted. A whole city is willing its team on. Everywhere outside London wants Coventry to win. It's the underdogs, the team spirit, against the expensive individualists.

City bounce back. They never know when they're beaten. It's the Spurs goal under pressure and the Spurs fans who start to whistle for half-time, whilst the city end sings louder and louder.

Town on Friday night was full of young people, singing, getting in the mood for the match.

Greens the Chemist has a window display in blue and white – cottonwool, Savlon, Optrex Eye Lotion, Super Softies baby wipes, potties and pregnancy tablets.

Let's Dance has blue and white leotards and pennants.

The second half sees City attack. They've tightened up in mid-field and tackle quicker, winning the ball more often. Spurs look on the rack. Gough and Mabbutt find it hard to deal with crosses, against Regis and Houchen. Pickering comes close.

Sillett senses the match going his way. We all know City can come from behind. That's the point, we all know how well the City have been playing. We aren't intimidated by the opposition. We remain confident.

Trevor Peake and Clive Allen practice their ballet routine on the pitch.

The pubs in town and throughout the city are draped in Sky Blue scarves and bunting. Pictures of the team are everywhere. Houses are decorated with streamers and balloons. Placards hang over doors, stickers are in car windows, posters adorn bedrooms and offices.

Houchen slips the ball out to Bennett on the right. Bennett dummies Thomas and sends in a cross. Houchen dives to reach it. He heads it home and City are level again. As the fans erupt and Houchen runs elated towards them, the Spurs players hang their heads in fatigue. They know and we know who is going to win.

It is all City now, pushing forward towards the huge bank of Sky Blue fans behind the Spurs' goal. McGrath and Gynn find more room in midfield as Spurs wilt and large gaps open up in their defence. Ardiles collapses with cramp. 'There's only one Brian Burrows' the crowd chant, in support of the injured player. It is that sort of atmosphere.

'Go For It, Go For It, City,
Sky Blues, Shooting to win,
Go For It, Go For It, City!'

The singing booms out across Wembley. The Spurs fans are silent. Mickey Gynn makes his presence felt with a series of penetrating runs through a flagging Tottenham defence.

'Here we go! Here we go!' waves around the stands and terraces. A great cup upset is happening. We all sense it.

The Council House is covered in bunting, union jacks and pennants, with "Good Luck City" along the windows and two large banners, one saying "Well Done Sky Blues" and the other "NALGO Says Well Done Sky Blues."

Shop assistants have been dressed in blue all week. In the Baker's Oven cake shop and restaurant, the staff are wearing caps and straw boaters with blue ribbons. 'Go For It' is being played non-stop around the city.

'If this is a dream, don't wake us up!'

There are blue and white striped plastic carrier bags, Davy Crockett hats and lads in City shirts. Dudley's Furniture Shop has sky blue lamp shades, banners and rosettes.

Kilcline clumsily tackles Mabbutt. He comes off worst and is soon substituted by Rodger. Full-time is nearly over. Mickey Gynn comes close to finishing it, but is beaten by Clemence.

The whistle goes and the players collapse. John Sillett harangues them, motivates them, implores them, tells them it's there to be won, whilst the physio slaps and massages tired leg muscles.

Ardiles is substituted by Stevens. Spurs look exhausted. City are the stronger team, they have a greater will to win.

'There's only one Mickey Gynn,' raises the roof.

The Cake Shop has made cakes in the shapes of a football, a rosette and a sky blue shirt, all in the City colours. West One, a trendy clothes shop, has its models in blue and white, with rosettes, caps and scarves.

Hammells, Walter Herbert and Gladdings all have displays. Chemists, butchers, travel agents, department stores, sweet shops, hardware stores all support the City. Pam the Florist has sprays of blue and white and two big blue elephants.

Jimmy Hill says: 'You can beat a team, but you can't beat a team and a city.'

Extra time is well under way. Rodger picks up the ball in the centre of Coventry's half. He boots it out to McGrath, who screams down the right, cutting in towards the Spurs penalty area. City forwards rush up. McGrath crosses fast and low. Mabbutt sticks out a leg. The ball hits his knee and skies over Clemence and into the net. Wembley erupts again!

'Here we go! Here we go! Here we go! booms out for the last twenty minutes of the match.

'Walk on, walk on, with hope in your heart, and you'll never walk alone, walk on . . . '

'Go For It!, Go For It, City.' The Coventry fans are irrepressible as they watch attack after attack launched against Spurs. 'Ole! Ole! Ole!' as the Sky Blues keep possession in the last minutes. A final Spurs attack, a missed cross, and it's all over. City have won the F.A. Cup!

A whole city celebrates. Children at home in their Sky Blue strip dance up and down, dogs bark, beer cans are waved, moggies are smothered in kisses. People come out onto the streets, dancing, doing congas and waving flags.

Kilcline painfully leads the team up the steps to the royal box, shakes hands and lifts the cup for a city. The Coventry end explodes in a welter of flags, scarves and cheers. The team dance around the pitch, showing their supporters the cup and pausing for photocalls. Dogs, having cursed extra time, finally get their walks, whilst the parks fill with kids who rush out with balls to imitate Bennett and Houchen.

Cars come out too, their horns parping and flags waving. Groups of supporters sing in the streets, waving at the cars.

A group of punks in leathers, tight skirts, fishnet tights, and mohican hairstyles sing in the road, draped in union jacks and waving cans of Breaker.

Kids stand on street corners smiling and cheering. A cyclist passes, streamers flying, his arms in the air, clapping his hands and shouting 'City! City! City!'

John Sillett and George Curtis hug Dave Bennett as he raises the cup.

A city forgets its depression, its closed factories, its dole queues and moves emotionally from rags to riches. It marks a more general change in the city, a grittier attitude as the boom gives way to a harsher struggle.

St Osburgs Road holds a street party with tables out for the kids, dancing and booming music.

A disabled girl in a wheelchair covered with balloons wears a city shirt, holds a large blue teddy and has a ghetto blaster hammering out 'Go For It City'. The boy pushing her has on a City cap, scarf and shirt.

A man comes out of the bookies, stuffing his winnings into his pocket.

The off-licences are open, doing a roaring trade.

A little girl pushes her doll's pram, covered in streamers.

At Wembley, the singing continues. 'They'll be there 'till the dogs start. Sillett'll come out of Trap Six.'

The shopping centres come alive with people buying last-minute groceries and with young people singing and waving flags.

People come out onto their balconies. The walkways of low-rise blocks see cheering and hugging. Joy-riding cars beep and screech, heading for town, or just driving around.

'The greatest day of my life.'

'Once in a life-time.'

'I was there.'

'Magic, pure magic.'

'I couldn't bear to miss it, it'd've been terrible.'

'It hasn't sunk in yet.'

Lady Godiva is draped in flags and a sign, "Coventry's Dream Day".

Wembley starts to empty. The team does interviews, then boards its coach. The M.1 belongs even more to the city as it becomes one long scene of jubilation.

'Welcome home, lads!'

London Road and Walsgrave Road turn out to cheer people returning. Bridges are garlanded with banners. Houses are decorated with bunting. Whole families forget themselves in the joyousness.

The cars return to join others circling the city centre, parping and cheering. People lean out of them, sit on the bonnets, walk between them, shake hands and sing. A whole city is letting off steam!

Mercia Sound replays the goals countless times, between "Go For It" and endless interviewing.

Coaches start to arrive back and people disembark in the city centre to enter the pubs, then stand outside with their glasses as they watch the celebrations.

Men dressed as Andy Pandies run around. Union Jacks and City flags are everywhere. Buses bring more people in. It is the night of the youth, the unemployed, the YTSer, the apprentice, the junior clerk.

An old man hobbles by with a walking stick. He wears a large rosette as his grandson, with a punk hairstyle, helps him along.

'Here we go, Here we go, Here we go !'

'There's only one Brian Burrows!'

'We are top of the Midlands!'

'There's only one Gary Mabbutt!'

A Viking, draped in a Union Jack, leans out of a car. A lad jumps from the back of a packed transit, kisses a girl in a car, then returns to kiss the driver – a man.

Lads are carrying girls. They congregate outside the Tally Ho, Coventry Cross and The Smithfield. Firecrackers explode. Girls walk by with blue spray in their hair. Some have blue and white faces. Hundreds sing and cheer by the fountain as horns sound, car bonnets are banged and people sing, 'Wembley, Wembley, Wemb-e-ley!'

Streets are crowded, girls dance in the fountain, beer cans are waved, cameras flash, scarves and flags sweep to and fro, people run arm in arm, cars are covered in foam slogans, everyone smiles. It's one o'clock Sunday morning.

Later that day, the team is driven over to show the cup to Brian Burrows in hospital. People start to stream into the city. There are hordes of them, with cars parked on every available space around the sealed-off city centre, hours before the players are due to arrive.

Cheers greet the team as the players board the open-top bus and there's a loud hurrah! as the cup emerges. Another bus has the youth team aboard.

Helicopters hover overhead and speed off like dragonflies. TV cameras, perched high on gantries, observe the scenes. The roads into the city centre are a continuous stream of people in white and blue.

Lady Godiva has four sitting tenants. She is covered in a banner and an anorak, with a blue and white chequered hat on.

People climb onto the parapet above Owen Owen's entrance, onto the roofs and across the multi-storied carparks.

The buses tour Walsgrave Hospital, where the nurses rush patients and children to the windows. They had held parties the day before on the wards. All the new babies in the maternity hospital are dressed in blue.

People line Walsgrave Road and the bridges over the ring-road, cheering and waving at the overwhelmed team.

That morning, the congregation at a local church had spontaneously burst into 'Go For It City' during the service.

Behind the first bus comes the second, with the youth team and the players' wives.

People climb trees and the Godiva clock. Two more heads accompany Peeping Tom's as he fixes his now permanent gaze on the packed crowd in Broad Gate. The mass of spectators begins on the outskirts of the city and goes right through to the centre, packing the route, ending in a huge crowd outside the Council house.

The tannoy blares out 'Go For It' and Forties' band music.

Whistles are blown, flags waved. A bloke on Lady Godiva shows off his Sky Blue underpants. It's the one ugly scene of the day.

A family licks ice creams, four-year-old twins and their elder brother, plus two adults, scoffing as they wait.

The buses crawl slowly through the jam-packed supporters in Corporation Street, up Trinity Street, through Broad Gate and struggle towards the Council House. All along, there are masses of people. A quarter of a million, at least. A whole city, waving at the team, staring in wonder at the cup, tears coming to their eyes, singing the Sky Blues' song, forgetting the past few years, just for a few days – the most glorious and happiest weekend in the city's history!